PROJECT

CONTROL

STANDARDS

PROJECT

CONTROL

STANDARDS

DICK H. BRANDON

MAX GRAY

BRANDON / SYSTEMS PRESS, INC

princeton   new york   london

iv

CONTENTS

List of Exhibits / vii

Section 1: Introduction and General Principles / 1

    1. The Philosophy of Project Control / 3

    2. Project Control Objectives / 11

    3. Environment and Scope / 17

    4. The System Development Process / 27

    5. The Basic Control Elements / 41

    6. The Project Control System / 51

Section 2: Procedures / 71

    7. Application Identification and Project Selection / 75

    8. The Priority System / 81

    9. Time Estimating and Project Planning / 85

    10. Personnel Assignment / 101

    11. Scheduling / 107

    12. Progress Reporting / 117

    13. Review and Progress Analysis / 121

    14. Cost Allocation / 127

Section 3: Project Control Documentation / 131

    15. Initiation and Estimating Documentation / 135

CONTENTS

16. Progress Documentation / 149

17. Control System Operating Documentation / 152

Section 4: Setting Up a Project Control System / 163

18. Preparatory Tasks / 165

19. The Project Control Manual / 169

20. Installation / 175

21. Post-Implementation Tasks and Maintenance / 179

Appendix

Software Packages for Project Control / 183

Bibliography

Recommended References / 193

PERT and CPM Bibliography / 195

Project Control Bibliography / 201

List of Exhibits

1. Management Planning Costs of System / 4
2. System Proposal Outline / 30
3. Analysis of Typical Control Points by Project Type / 38
4. Application Identification and Project Selection / 77
5. Sample Task List / 86
6. Project Management Responsibility Chart / 88
7. Time Relationship for Task 3—Coding / 93
8. Construction of Time Relationships / 96
9. Sample Skills Matrix / 102
10. Sample Staff Selection Matrix / 103
11. Sample Gantt Chart / 109
12. Sample Network for a System Development Project / 111
13. Checklist for Test Planning / 114
14. Table of Contents—System Test Plan / 115
15. Table of Contents—Program Test Plan / 116
16. Progress Reporting Checkpoints / 118
17. Review and Control Guide for Selected Checkpoints / 122
18. User Request / 136
19. Resource Requirements Forecast / 138
20. System Development Estimate Guide / 140
21. Program Development Estimate Completion Form / 144
22. The Estimate Summary / 145
23. Project Task Plan and Schedule / 147
24. Individual Hours Recap / 150
25. Progress Report / 152
26. Project Review Form / 154
27. Checkpoint Report / 157
28. Monthly Operator Report / 158
29. Monthly Equipment Usage Report / 159
30. Completed Project Report / 160
31. Project Control Document Checklist / 161
32. Project Control Manual: Suggested Table of Contents / 170
33. Distribution Record for Project Control Manual / 176
34. Revision Page for Project Control Manual / 180

SECTION 1

INTRODUCTION AND GENERAL PRINCIPLES

1/ THE PHILOSOPHY OF PROJECT CONTROL

The cost of delays and waste caused by poor control of the system development process is incalculable. The purpose of this book is to provide data processing managers with a guide to the general principles, techniques, and development of a project control system. The book is based on the belief that data processing management techniques have not kept pace with the phenomenal economic and technological growth of the data processing business.

Technological advances of the last sixteen or seventeen years are probably well known to those concerned with computers in any capacity. We have progressed in hardware from the enormous, unwieldy tube machines of the early fifties, which had at best a range of three types of peripherals, to the elaborate solid state circuiting and wide range of peripherals of the third generation computers in use today. In the field of software, we have progressed from machine coding (with the program held on a 'high speed' drum) to the use of sophisticated high level languages, operating systems, multi-tasking, and multiprogramming. In systems techniques, we have a far greater range of possibilities in designing a system, compared to the inescapable serial batch processing of the last decade.

For example, incredible as it might seem to young people just entering the field today, there was a time when the most efficient method of sorting the records on a reel of tape was to punch the data onto Hollerith cards, sort the cards on EAM equipment, and then read the cards back into the computer to put the data back on tape in the desired sequence. The 'good old days,' perhaps, but *not* dating back to our grandfather's time or even our father's; it is within the memory of the current generation of data processing managers. Compare that tedious process to the high-speed disks and hyper-tapes, the variety of sorting techniques to choose from, the wide variety of parameters that may be specified for packaged sort programs, and the easy 'sort' commands of high-level languages available today!

But with all these advances, the management of data processing installations is as inadequate today as it was fifteen years ago, if not more so. The trouble is compounded by the fact that larger and larger percentages of a company's total operating costs are being spent on data processing; business has become so dependent on computers that if they were all to grind to a halt tomorrow, so would the American economy, at least temporarily. Exhibit 1 illustrates some of these costs.

Yet it is in the area of management that data processing has had the greatest potential expertise to draw upon, from other areas of

Exhibit 1:   Management Planning Costs of System

DEVELOPMENT COSTS		ANNUAL EQUIPMENT COSTS	
Site	$35,000	4 tape drives	
Training (direct)	10,000	2 disks	$9,000/month
Initial Supplies	10,000	20,000 characters	= $108,000
Facilities and Furniture	15,000	of storage	
Test Time	5,000		
Systems Design (10 man-years @ $12,000 inclusive of training & fringe)	120,000	Printer	$500/month
		Card Reader Punch	= 6,000
		TOTAL	$114,000
Programming (15 man-years @ $10,000 inclusive)	150,000		
Conversion	40,000	ANNUAL PERSONNEL COSTS	
Installation (4 months duplex	92,000	(Operating)	
(Subtotal)	477,000	DP Manager (½)	8,000
Money Cost (6%, 5 years, straight line = 15% of $477,000)	72,000	Operations Mgr.	11,000
		Analyst	13,000
		Programmer	11,000
TOTAL	$549,000	Secretary	6,000
		4 Operators	24,000
		6 Key Punch Operators	27,000
		2 Peripheral Operators	12,000
		1 Schedulor	8,000
		(Subtotal)	120,000
		20% Fringe	24,000
		TOTAL	$144,000

SUMMARY OF COSTS

Equipment	$114,000
Personnel	114,000
Supplies	20,000
Development (÷ 5)	110,000
TOTAL ANNUAL COST	$388,000

commerce and industry. In only an extremely limited way—for example, in the reluctant adoption of critical path analysis by a few courageous operations research managers—have we turned to proven techniques developed by others. Current issues of computer journals and technical magazines are pounced upon and avidly scanned in every data processing department in the country; but the few articles they contain which are written about data processing *management* are at best superficial and at worst incomprehensible, and so we have largely given up reading them. However, one rarely sees a copy of a recognized management magazine (such as the *Harvard Business Review, Fortune, or Forum* or others of good quality) in a data processing department library. And in no sense can it be said that data processing people have been innovators in management, except in that we sometimes seem to be trying not to manage at all.

The causes of this situation are no great mystery. They are two-fold: The first lies in the unprecedented growth rate of the data processing industry itself. When the first generation of hardware was rapidly succeeded by the second and then the third, when one conversion was barely finished before the next had to be begun, when computer technology was revolutionized overnight not once, but again and again, when data processing budgets—and the pressure to get badly needed systems on the air willy-nilly—increased geometrically, when computer purchase or rental often represented the single biggest item in a company's operating budget so that to let the equipment stand idle was a cardinal sin, and when we didn't even have time for the simplest *documentation* of what we had done, who had the time for "fancy" management techniques? Not data processing! Today, it is recognized that a stitch in time might have saved the payroll disaster.

The second cause is found in the environment in which the initial development of computers and data processing techniques took place. The early computer men were not managers and did not represent themselves to be. They worked in semi-scientific, usually academic, surroundings. It was the engineers and scientists who introduced us to data processing; no one can fault them for neglecting to mention that other skills might be necessary to the economic utilization of their wonderful computing machines. Specific management functions do not always exist in an academic environment, and it is that heritage which contributes to today's lacks.

The time has come to cut our links with that heritage. Today, if we look at how the costs of an installation are apportioned, we find that an increasing percentage of the money allocated to data processing functions is being spent on research and development — systems and programming — rather than on computers and other hardware. In fact, the proportionate cost of hardware and computer operations is decreasing while the cost of systems development is increasing.* The people in the systems development areas are therefore becoming more responsible for a greater portion of the costs of an installation.

The Manager's Assets

The major assets of systems development managers are no longer machines, but people. Hardware and software may be discounted as *tools*; the only real *assets* are people. Good staff are hard to come by, difficult to train, and always seem to leave just when one needs them most; they command what to our elders would have been exorbitant salaries, and can afford to be difficult to work with. But the shortage of good programmers and systems analysts will not be easing in the foreseeable future. To get the best possible results, therefore, it is necessary to get the best possible results from people rather than from machines.

Thus, in the management of programming and systems, we should be concerned less with the programs and the systems and more with the *people* who design the systems and the *people* who write the programs. They are our major resource, and at once our major problem.

The Definition of "Management"

With this in view, what then is management? More specifically, what is good data processing management? To begin, data processing management is too often performed by technicians. Supervisory and management positions in data processing are usually filled by the best technicians — the best programmer is promoted to programming supervisor, the best systems analyst becomes the assistant department manager, and then the manager. They may be expert technicians, but are they necessarily the best managers?

The manager's functions have been defined well by Peter Drucker:

*See Dick Brandon, *Management Planning for Data Processing,* Princeton: Brandon/Systems Press, 1970, Exhibit 10.2 p. 145.

"The manager is the dynamic, life-giving element in every business. Without his leadership the resources of production remain resources and never become production. In a competitive economy, above all, the quality and performance of the managers determine the success of the business, indeed they may determine the survival." — *Management by Objectives.*

To become the "life-giving element," data processing management must begin to manage people. The day of the technician as manager is over, unless the technician can learn the skills and techniques of management.

Another unfortunate element of current data processing management which requires change is the tendency toward 'management by the seat of the pants.' This is the method in which events control the managers, rather than the other way around. It is a situation where there is never any real control; it is management by reaction, not action. *We must learn to control rather than to react.*

The good data processing manager needs, then, qualities of leadership, and the ability to control the data processing environment. If it were necessary to quantify the source of these abilities, one could say that good management is 90% plain, ordinary common sense, combined with a set of rules or techniques which can cover most situations that arise. Some good managers, with no formal training, have discovered these facts by themselves — one might say that they manage by instinct. For most of us, however, it is helpful to have them carefully formulated. The first step is to consider the three most important functions of a data processing manager.

Functions of Management

Function 1   To acquire the best assets available, to improve them, and to keep them.

Because the major assets of a data processing installation are people, a significant portion of the data processing manager's time must be devoted to recruiting, selecting, and training his staff. It has been only recently that the personnel departments in some companies have come to realize the special problems that are associated with hiring and training operators, programmers, and systems analysts. Because of the particular characteristics required for success in the field, the lack of any really adequate means of identifying these, and the acute shortage of good people, the data processing manager (more than the managers in other departments in the company) is required to take an especially active role in obtaining and training the staff he needs.

Function 2   To provide a good working environment for the performance of the data processing department's services to the company.

This means that the manager must do more than see to it that the computer room is kept at the proper temperature and humidity and that crumbs don't get into the data cell mechanism. It means good working conditions for the staff as well. It means having and using good data processing methods and performance standards, so that day-to-day tasks can be performed in a predetermined manner and so that all personnel are evaluated by the same known criteria. One often hears the argument that because programmers are 'creative' people, it is not fair, nor even possible, to impose standardized working methods. On the contrary, standards relieve the programmer of the necessity for making mundane decisions about the details of his work, and leave him free to apply his talents where they are really needed — in logical analysis and intricate problem solution. Experience has shown that morale increases and staff turnover decreases in installation that have and use flexible, workable methods and performance standards. There is a great deal of uncertainty inherent in the data processing environment by the very nature of the job to be done; standards provide a base of stability everyone can appreciate.

Function 3   To ensure that resources are applied in an efficient manner and to monitor and control their performance to produce a *good* product on *time*, within *budget*.

It is easy to forget that in any company the data processing department is a *service* organization. Unlike, for example, the sales department, whose ultimate goal is to sell more of the company's product, or the production units, whose job is to make it, the existence of the data processing department is justified only through the services it performs for other departments of the company. It is therefore the data processing manager's responsibility to ensure that his department fulfills its mission by producing the required data processing systems,

— at an economical rate,
— of good quality, and
— on time.

This book is concerned with function 3 and peripherally with function 2 as a prerequisite. A set of carefully formulated rules for allocating and controlling resources is required to accomplish that function; that is *project control*.

Control System Characteristics

A good, workable project control system will have certain characteristics. It will
- be simple in concept,
- do what it is intended to do,
- be suited to the needs of the organization,
- be easy to implement, and
- be flexible.

The solution to a complex problem need not always be complex itself. The problems a project control system is designed to solve may, in fact, *seem* more complex than they really are just because the installation is so deeply mired in them. In any case, it is certainly not necessary to introduce another set of complicated problems via an intricate project control system. The type of system recommended here is based on one simple idea: the checkpoint, which breaks the development process into small, controllable tasks. The system development process has built into it a number of work turn-over points, which can be easily utilized as control checkpoints as well. A complete discussion is given in the remaining chapters of this section, particularly in Chapter 4, "The System Development Process."

It may seem obvious to say that a good project control system will do what it is intended to do, but the hard truth is that many other types of systems designed and implemented by data processing departments do *not*. If this is to be cured, the control system must itself be effective. All of the ramifications of the over-all goal of monitoring and controlling resources are discussed in the chapter on objectives which follows.

The system must also be designed with the particular needs of the individual organization in mind. It is not possible to produce a single, completely designed system that will fulfill the needs of everyone. Consequently, the techniques and procedures outlined in this book are intended as guidelines, not doctrine. Chapter 3, "Environment and Scope," discusses the major variations which need to be taken into account.

The easier the new project control system is to implement, the sooner it will be in operation and the more readily it will be accepted. It thus becomes doubly important that the system be designed to fit in with current methods and practices. Section IV of the book covers procedures for implementing a project control system.

Lastly, the system must be flexible, for two reasons: to make it amenable to change, and to make it enforceable. No system can be cast in concrete, and project control must be able to change as the structure and needs of the data processing department change. And it is extremely important that the manager not be turned into a policeman by project control; in fact, a good control system may well let him step *down* from that role by giving him adequate control without the necessity for constant discipline. Again, for this reason project control procedures must fill in with other standard practices of the department, rather than be imposed upon them willy-nilly.

The remaining chapters in this section discuss in detail the background to development of a project control system. Section II gives practical techniques needed by the manager to design and use a control system. Section III outlines recommended documents. These may be referenced elsewhere in the book, but most of the actual examples are given here. Section IV shows the steps in developing and implementing a project control system. The various appendices list items that may be of interest for further study.

2/ PROJECT CONTROL OBJECTIVES

The application of systems and information handling techniques assists the manger of any organization in making the decisions that determine the organization's efficiency, effectiveness and profitability. The data processing group, while functioning primarily in a service capacity, can nevertheless have a profound influence on the ultimate success or failure of the business. Unfortunately, data processing system designers are frequently guilty of the same inadequate practices that the data processing systems were designed to correct. The goals of the individual project may ultimately be met, but to what purpose? Many of us suspect, although we may admit it only to ourselves in the dark of night, that perhaps the company would have been better off if we, the data processing people, had not got our hands on the systems in the first place.

Today, it is the rule rather than the exception that we miss completion dates, exceed budgets — often by a large margin — and, worse, when finished find that the final product not only fails to come up to the original specification but is so poorly designed and constructed that even justifiable maintenance costs far in excess of its value. These situations are so common that many of us accept them as inevitable.

These same unfortunate results in other areas of a business would cause research and development people to exclaim, "What they need are controls." If data processing professionals are to assist management by providing mature information systems, we must apply control principles first to the management of data processing projects. The return on investment of resources in project control will far outweigh the cost. The amount of money saved by good control techniques will depend on the size of the organization, the total investment in data processing, the quality of management, and the extent of the need.

The proper use of available resources — primarily people, but also including equipment, time, and money — can have an enormous impact on the installation cost of a system. Over-runs on system development of 100% are common, and even 300% over-runs are encountered with alarming frequency. If adequate project control can reduce by even a small percentage the total time taken to completion, therefore, substantial cost reductions could be enjoyed. Further, cost over-runs are probably less significant than time over-runs. If the system being developed is intended to save $100,000 annually in clerical costs, or increase profitability by $500,000, then several months delay in implementation can represent losses far in excess of the cost of the expended resources, and certainly in excess of the total cost of installing the project control system itself.

The general objective of a project control system is the production of data processing systems that meet the user's need, at the right price, and on time — through the proper application of monitoring and control techniques.

More specifically, a project control system should enable us to
— predict future needs at any stage in the project,
— evaluate personnel performance,
— evaluate planning, scheduling, estimating, and budgeting techniques,
— judge the quality of the product being produced,
— evaluate the control system itself, and
— focus attention on problems *in time to do something about them.*

The importance of the last item far outweighs all the others combined.

Predicting Future Needs

The control system should enable us, at any stage of the project, to predict future requirements for systems work, programming, clerical man-days, total elapsed time, and/or computer utilization, and to do it reliably. Two features of project control contribute to this: the first is segmentation of the work to be done into units, or tasks, small enough to allow accurate predictions; the second is the availability of statistics relating to needs of past tasks of a similar nature, and a historical record of the accuracy of past predictions. Ideally, the project control system will let the manager constantly check his past performance in estimating requirements to show him in what areas and by how much his estimates tend to be wrong, thus serving as a learning tool.

Evaluating Personnel Performance

By providing standard units of comparison and a method for establishing in advance what is expected of each person on each task, it becomes possible to evaluate an individual's performance in comparison with an acknowledged standard, with his past performance on similar tasks and with the performance of others. Further, if a person's work is *not* measuring up to standard for whatever reason, this fact becomes known soon enough to allow effective corrective action to be taken. Similarly, if an individual is working better and faster than expected, the results can be taken into consideration when planning future stages of the project, as well as being accurately reflected in his record.

As a side effect, morale will increase as staff members realize they are being judged fairly by standardized measures. They will adapt more readily to the requirements of the project control system and cooperate to ensure its success.

Evaluating Techniques

Similarly, the utilization of standard measures and past history will allow management to measure the effectiveness of the techniques they have been using for planning, scheduling, estimating, and budgeting. While it is not possible to produce a $50,000 system for $35,000 no matter how good the planning and budgeting is, it will be possible to separate the failure (or success) of management, management's techniques, and the resources themselves from each other, in order to pinpoint exactly where the difficulty lies.

Evaluating the Product

Quality control (discussed more fully in Chapter 5) is an important aspect of project control. A look ahead at Exhibit 3 in Chapter 5 will show the frequent intervals at which quality control checks should be built into the system development process. As we are ultimately judged by the users we serve on the quality of the product produced, this aspect of the project control process cannot be over-emphasized. It is the segmentation of work into tasks, with accompanying checkpoints, that allows quality to be carefully and constantly evaluated throughout the system development process, and even after the system has been installed and "turned over" to the user.

Evaluating the Project Control System

In the long run, the effectiveness of the project control system may be judged on how well it enables management to fulfill their functions, and on how well it meets the objectives outlined. The failure of a project control system may be due to any one of a large number of factors, some of which are

— inflexibility of the system,
— lack of cooperation from staff,
— lack of commitment from management, or
— failure of the system to mesh with other aspects of the department's operations.

The first and last points have already been discussed; cooperation and commitment are covered in the next chapter.

A more likely event will be that the control system performs less well in some areas than in others. If the system has been designed with this possibility in mind, it will be easy to pin-point and change the weak aspects.

Warning of Trouble

The last major objective listed, and by far the most important, is that a good project control system will warn management of approaching trouble in time to permit an effective response. Frequent checkpoints will highlight slippage and/or poor product quality as soon as they begin to occur; task segmentation will make it easy to identify the cause. Further, the technique of committing one's resources in stages (explained in detail later) allows flexibility in taking corrective action.

This benefit may nonplus the small minority of managers who excuse the poor performance of their department by saying they didn't know anything was wrong until it was too late. For the majority of concerned data processing managers, it will provide a much-welcomed tool to help them do their jobs more effectively.

Other side effects are, first, that the manager will be able to project his workload figures far enough ahead to be able to see slack periods coming up in time to adjust schedules. There will not be weeks when everyone is sitting around doing nothing (except complaining), followed by periods of frantic activity when everyone *would* complain if they had the time. It is even possible that substantial cost savings from reduced overtime will be realized.

Second, the manager will be freed from his policing role and will be able to delegate responsibility, not only for project control activities but for others under his jurisdiction as well, so that he may more truly become a *manager*, rather than merely reacting to one emergency situation after another.

Lastly, the project control system will impose a certain degree of beneficial discipline on the organization. In many data processing departments the elimination of absolute anarchy, while at first ruffling a few ardent discontents, is enough of an end in itself to justify any control system.

3/ ENVIRONMENT AND SCOPE

The details of the project control system implemented will obviously have to vary from one organization to another. Some of the more important factors which will influence the final design are

— the size and business of the company,
— the size of the data processing organization,
— the organization of the data processing department(s), and
— the characteristics of typical projects.

The level and complexity of the controls instituted in one organization may be entirely unworkable in a different environment. Because each data processing department must pick and choose from among the variety of methods and degrees of complexity available, the impact of these factors is discussed below.

The Company

As a basic factor, one of the most important influences on the project control system that is developed will be the general policies and business environment of the company. A governmental or military installation will already have a fairly well-defined set of standard practices, actively enforced. A project control system for such an organization will also tend to be relatively rigid, detailed, and easy to enforce. A small service company, on the other hand, will have a minimum of stringent requirements in work procedures and will require a less detailed, more flexible control system.

However, size in itself does not necessarily imply an extensive project control system. Decentralized companies who allow their various operating units to carry on more or less independently may have control problems resembling more those of smaller organizations. The decentralization of data processing organizations is discussed more fully below.

Finally, the type of business the company is engaged in, in that that factor influences the conduct of all its business activities, will have an effect on project control measures. Financial organizations, for example, will already have a certain discipline inherent in the working environment due to the necessity of complying with a large number of governmental and industry regulations. This degree of discipline must be carried over into the data processing sections if they are to successfully fulfill their role of providing services to the user departments.

The Data Processing Department

The size and organization of the data processing department will have a particularly strong influence on the form of the project control system devised. A small, centralized organization in which all functions of the company's data processing activities are carried out will require a less complex system. Because there are fewer levels of responsibility, the number of checkpoints need not be as great as in an organization with a large number of reporting lines. Communications between functions are easier, so the amount of documentation needed will be less.

In a large company with a number of sub-divisions of data processing functions—for example, separate units for operations research, software development, applications development of various types, and with a separate machine operations unit—the more complex lines of communication will require more checkpoints and correspondingly more documentation for project control.

Decentralized systems and programming functions, where each geographical unit operates independently, present special problems. Depending on data processing policy and the types of projects undertaken by each unit, one of three approaches can be taken.

(1) A project control system can be developed and implemented at one installation, then put into use at the others.

(2) Each unit can make its own decisions and proceed independently, although this will involve a duplication of effort.

(3) All units can act in concert and use one system suitable for all, whenever possible.

The second approach will probably result in less extensive project control procedures, because only the needs of one unit have to be considered, and because the department can then be thought of as a relatively small organization.

Various approaches to developing and implementing the control systems are discussed in more detail in Section 4 .

Project Characteristics

The size and complexity of a project control system will depend on the characteristics of the projects normally under development. The most important are the length of time required for development and the size of the project teams. Development documentation is important as a guide in assessing project progress, one of the objectives of the project control system. Control of a lengthy project will be better if more detailed types of documentation are produced at more frequent intervals. Similarly, the need for control increases as the number of people assigned to the project increases. Where there are more opportunities for something to go wrong, and where the consequences of slippage are more serious, control procedures must be more stringent and checkpoints more frequent.

In an organization where the projects to be carried out are somewhat circumscribed—for example, where heavy reliance is placed on the use of software packages developed by outside sources, requiring a minimum of systems analysis and programming, or where the functions of the data processing department are limited to the replacement of clerical systems, and exclude the development of new types of operational procedures — then the number of tasks and consequent number of checkpoints needed will be reduced, as will the average length of time spent on each project.

The environment in which the control system will be operating, therefore, has an important influence on the nature and extent of the control procedures to be used.

REQUIREMENTS FOR PROJECT CONTROL

In addition to the general environment, however, there are a number of closely related factors which have a direct bearing on the nature and scope of any project control system. They are

—the extent of management commitment,
—data processing management "salesmanship,"
—the existence of data processing standards,
—user participation, and
—an automation committee.

Indeed, these factors will have an important influence on the success or failure of the system, and even on the decision of whether or not to develop a project control system at all.

Management Commitment

Management commitment is the degree to which management realizes the necessity for effective project control measures, and to which they are willing to support it. It includes *all* levels of management, from top corporate officers down to and including data processing management and technical data processing supervisors.

There can be no effective project control system without the support of management. Data processing management and the executive office to which it reports must formally proclaim as policy the procedures and obligations required for precise control over data processing projects and the resources applied to such projects.

Implied in this commitment is that management at all levels will

- make available the necessary personnel (on an uninterrupted assignment for the time required) to develop, enforce, and monitor the control system,
- review the reports generated and take timely corrective actions as required,
- accept the disciplines embodied in a project control system,
- accept the requirement for participation in reviewing budget estimates,
- accept responsibility for participating in the assignment of priorities, and
- not violate the procedures for establishing such priorities.

In some companies the attitude of top management seems to be that any money not actually spent on systems and programming is of doubtful value. This must be overcome. Management must be convinced that an effective project control system will pay for itself in the long term (possibly even in the short term) and will result in better, cheaper information systems delivered *on time*.

The commitment of data processing management is just as vital as that of top corporate management. It is they who must develop and implement the system, and enforce it once it is in operation. Staff members cannot be expected to cooperate in the effort if their bosses have an obvious bias against the undertaking from the first.

We cannot "pull our punches" in a project of this nature, or it will be doomed from the start. The key to a successful project control system is support from all levels of management right from the beginning.

Salesmanship

Salesmanship is closely related to management commitment. In determining the success of a project control system, it is a particularly important ability for data processing managers. It is not enough for the data processing manager to be committed to control procedures — he must also be able to sell the concept to others. There are three groups within the company he will have to deal with: top corporate management, the data processing staff, and the users of data processing services.

It will usually be the data processing manager's job to prove to top management the necessity and justification for a project control system. He will have to prepare the initial proposal for it (or direct its preparation) and convince corporate management that it is worth spending money on. He will play an important role in gaining their commitment for the system.

The task of convincing staff of the desirability of control procedures is just as vital. The attitude of the systems analysts and programmers who are ultimately affected by project control will often mean the difference between success or failure. The manager must not simply announce that henceforth these measures will be in effect, or they are sure to be resented. He must explain their function and benefits, and gain the backing of all members of his staff.

Although less important, the attitude of users toward a project control system should not be overlooked. If we say to user management, "Your system could be on the air a few weeks sooner, except that at the moment we need the manpower to develop our own new control system," or, after it is in effect, "we wouldn't need to take the time to produce this document if it weren't for the project control system," we are bound to generate resistance. It will be worth the time taken to inform users of the purpose and nature of the project control system to sell it to them as well as to top management and the data processing department staff.

Standards

Data processing standards are a formal set of rules and guidelines, usually embodied in a manual issued to all staff members, which specify the policies, procedures and practices of the activities carried out by the department. These include particularly procedures and practices which govern all of the tasks dealing with systems development and implementation.

Without standards of this kind, no project control system is possible. They provide a common frame of reference for the performance of all tasks, and thereby provide a common base for estimating resource requirements, reviewing the expenditure of such resources (people, time, money, and equipment), and determining the reasons for performance deficiency.

To illustrate the necessity of standards for an effective project control system, take the example of checkpoint control at the end of the system specification phase. It would be impossible to determine the adequacy of the specifications unless a recognized set of rules existed for their development and presentation. The same can be said for all tasks in the system development process.

If no such set of standards exists in the installation, the development of a project control system must be postponed until they are created. Such an undertaking will then be the first phase of developing the project control system.

User Participation

In addition to being "sold" on the merits of project control, user personnel have a role in the workings of the system. The participation of users in the total system development process is vitally important. Three phases of the process where their work is most important are: when a system is initially specified, during data gathering, and at system test and implementation time (see Chapter 4, "The System Development Process"). It should be kept in mind that the data processing system is built for and belongs to the user, *not* to the data processing department. It must be designed to serve his needs first, not the convenience of systems analysts and programmers.

At the very beginning of a new development project, a user staff member (or, if warranted by the size and scope of the system, a group) should be nominated to serve as liaison to the project team. He should have two primary qualifications; he should

— be thoroughly familiar with the application being implemented, and
— have the authority to make all necessary decisions.

The first point speaks for itself, and is not directly concerned with project control. The second is more important, from our point of view. It is recommended that user authorization be obtained at certain key checkpoints in the system development process, notably when the system specification is completed, when the system test plan is drawn up, and at the conclusion of system testing. The user team member must know in advance that he is expected to review the work done at each of these checkpoints, and to authorize continuance of the project. The success of the final system will depend on his acumen and knowledge of the application. If the authorization is taken as a mere formality, no proper review will be conducted. The user personnel must be impressed with the importance of the decisions.

Further, he must have formal authority to make these decisions. The initials of a user participant on the cover of an inadequate set of specifications will provide no shelter at all for the data processing department if, when problems turn up, top management points out that the individual had no authority to give the go-ahead. It must be clearly recognized by all that such authority does exist, and that the corresponding responsibility rests with the user department. Again, it is important to remember that the application system *belongs* to the user.

The Automation Committee

Linked to the three previous requirements is the establishment of an automation committee. This body already exists in some companies; it may be called a steering committee, a data processing advisory committee, or the like. In general, its function is to guide and coordinate the implementation of data processing systems.

The data processing department has an unusual relationship with other departments of a company. It is not (or should not) be in a position to set policy, yet it has a profound influence on the way in which other departments carry out their functions. The department should be governed, therefore, from the top levels of company management; at the same time, it is logical that the departments which it serves should also be informed of and have a say in its activities. Thus, the automation committee.Some specific function of the automation committee will be to

—review the scope of data processing within the company,
— set long-term goals for the data processing department,
— set and review budgets,
— select and authorize systems development projects, establish priorities,
— select and authorize projects internal to the data processing department, such as equipment purchases and projects like the project control system, and
— periodically review the department's progress.

The chairman should be the corporate officer to whom the data processing manager reports. He should be a senior manager with direct responsibility for all data processing activities in the company, and with *no* special interest in any one department that uses the computer services. Other members of the committee will include the data processing manager and representatives of live management of the user departments.

The automation committee will be responsible for developing a long-range data processing program. The program should be an overall plan for design and implementation of information handling systems. Data processing management is responsible for constructing the initial version of this plan. The automation commitee reviews and approves it, resolving competitive requirements for resources in joint discussions with the users. The plan must include

— a list of anticipated new systems,
— a tentative schedule for their implementation,
— a list of operational systems which will require maintenance and other sustaining efforts, and
— a catalog of systems to be converted from one processing form or mode to another.

The long-range plan should identify the projects to which resource commitments must be made. It will also indicate the time-frame within which these events will take place, and will document project priorities.

It is within this framework that the project control system will operate. The two-fold thesis of project control—review of work done to date at frequent intervals, and planning ahead—presupposes the existence of such a plan.

The automation committee will obviously have a special role in influencing the final form of the project control system—and in ensuring that the system is adhered to.

Summary

To summarize, the variables of the data processing environment must be considered when determining the form and scope of a project control system; at the same time, there is a requirement for certain basics if the system is to be a success. These include management commitment at all levels, the ability of data processing management to sell its ideas, data processing standards, and user participation in all phases of system development. The establishment of an automation committee, if one does not already exist, is also highly recommended.

ong range plan

standards $\longrightarrow$ project mgmt

1) what is to be done
   when
   why
   by whom

2) how is it to be done

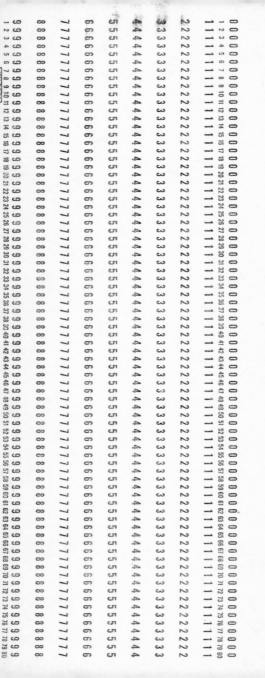

4/ THE SYSTEM DEVELOPMENT PROCESS

The technique of project control depends on an understanding of the system development process. If the basic principle of continuing control is to be applied, the manager must know at what points in the development process review of progress is necessary. It is not enough to determine that the system is working (or not working) after it has been installed, or even during final testing; it is of no use whatsoever to learn that the project is three months behind schedule when it is too late to do anything about it. And it will be much more costly to discover that important elements were overlooked by the systems analyst after the programming has been completed; to discover on the day of installation that the team has neglected to prepare adequate documentation for operation of the programs.

A previously defined series of standard tasks will also facilitate comparison of one project to another. It will be possible to use historical information about past projects to refine estimates for future projects or those in progress. Further, with standard statistics available for determining whether improvement has been made in the estimating and budgeting of projects, the manager has a tool for measuring his own progress in the use of project control techniques, and for measuring the benefits of the control system itself.

It is also important to have a standard series of tasks to which job functions and responsibilities may be related. It must be clearly defined to each member of each project team where responsibility for task completion and review rests. Where the responsibility is a joint one, this must be defined also.

Eleven phases of system development are generally recognized. They are divided among the three categories of Project Initiation, Project Fulfillment, and Project Completion. The break-down may be modified to suit the needs of an individual installation. Each of the eleven steps should be further sub-divided as needed; for example, programming can be segmented into specification review, block diagramming, coding, desk-checking, test planning, testing, and documentation.

The eleven steps, described below, apply to a long-term development project. Some may be abbreviated or eliminated for short-term, maintenance, and rescue projects. In this context, long-term development means development of a permanent new system, even if the new system is merely replacing an already automated one. It will, by definition, be of long duration and/or require the use of a large percentage of the installation's personnel, and in its course will follow the total sequence of phases given below. A short-term development project is a new system, but one which can be completed in a short time or with few personnel. These are often "one-time" systems, such as conversion packages, or "one-program" systems, such as specially developed utility programs for in-house use. Maintenance (also called modification) refers to planned changes to an operational system which go through the complete system development process from initial request through analysis, programming, and system test, although usually on a smaller scale. Rescue maintenance refers to changes required on an emergency basis, usually due to the discovery of an error in the system design or programming, or due to the imposition of special requirements by government agencies or other regulatory bodies. These usually begin at the late system analysis or programming stage, and do not always require a full system test upon completion.

With these definitions in mind, then, the eleven phases, or steps of system development, are

PROJECT INITIATION
  1 Application identification and project selection
  2 System survey
PROJECT FULFILLMENT
  3 Data gathering
  4 System analysis
  5 System design
  6 Programming
  7 Program testing
  8 System testing
PROJECT COMPLETION
  9 Converstion and installation
  10 System maintenance
  11 System evaluation.

1. Application Identification and Project Selection

The selection of applications for automation should be made by the automation or applications committee, although new ideas for research and development projects may originate from any of the various departments or branches of a company. Potential projects generated from the operating level are normally reviewed before any decision is made regarding selection. The idea may be immediately rejected if it is obviously not feasible or if it is already being planned. If the data processing manager thinks the idea may have some merit, he may have a preliminary technical study performed by a systems analyst. The idea will then await review and approval by the committee. If the application is feasible, but involves policy decisions, the implications should be considered and documented.

Approval by the committee implies authorization for assignment of personnel and for work to be begun, or continued, on the first phases. It is not now possible to determine exactly how long the development process will require and exactly how much it will cost, but it will be possible to make a general estimate. (Estimating techniques are discussed in Chapter 9.) During each of the early phases of system development, refined, realistic estimates of the cost and time needed for the next phase can be developed. It is at these checkpoints that management can decide whether to go ahead with the system as originally conceived, to modify the scope, or to shelve the project.

2. System Survey

A System Survey determines the economic, operational, and technical desirability of automating the application. It is usually a joint responsibility of the systems analysis function and the management of operating activities, but may also call upon the services of programming and operating technicians and of various specialists within the operating departments.

Documentation of the results of this phase, the system proposal, is of critical importance. It must include

- preliminary system design alternatives,
- recommendations and justification,
- comparison with present methods, and
- equipment requirements.

A recommended outline for the system proposal is given in Exhibit 2.

The department responsible for data processing research and development initiates a review of the system proposal. The user departments (the beneficiaries of the system) also participate. The review enables data processing personnel to clarify the objectives of the system and to explore all implications of the problem to be solved. Each user department involved in the system designates an official contact for the project. The user contact should be a person who understands his department's needs in relation to the system being developed, and who is vested with the authority and responsibility for decisions about system functions.

If the proposal is approved and authorization for the project obtained, personnel are assigned to the fulfillment phases of the project.

Exhibit 2: System Proposal Outline

1.0 Introduction
    1.1 Scope of Study
    1.2 Methods Used
    1.3 Premises and Assumptions
2.0 Management Summary
    2.1 Findings: Current Environment
    2.2 Information Requirements
    2.3 Cost Comparisons
    2.4 Recommended Course of Action
3.0 Design Alternatives
4.0 Proposed System Description
5.0 Outline Implementation Plan and Schedule
6.0 Exhibits and Appendices

3. Data Gathering

The data processing department can then begin detailed research and analysis. The scope of this phase will vary widely, depending on the type of project under development and on the state of existing documentation. A straight conversion of a well documented system to another machine or language, without changes to the functions of the system, will require almost no effort in data gathering. At the other extreme, to develop a large new system to perform functions now being done manually will probably require more work in data gathering than in any other phase. The description given below applies mainly to the larger effort.

During this phase, data processing personnel will study existing procedures and policy, including operating rules. If the system under development is replacing a clerical system, procedures describing the present operation may exist only in the minds of a few supervisors. Interviewing must be heavily relied upon. Extracting a description of an existing system under such circumstances requires consummate skill and infinite patience.

If the system being replaced is already wholly or partially automated, some documentation will already exist, and the data processing department will collect information from operating instructions, programming documentation (if any), user manuals, and any other existing documents describing the processes and functions of the current system. Other sources of information are current reports, files, work flow charts, job descriptions, organization charts, and statements, regulations, and requirements imposed by governments, unions, customers, or other contracts.

Information regarding the technical implications of automating is then assembled. The schedule requirements of the user departments must be evaluated for compatibility with the existing computer operations schedule. Information must be gathered on the possible problems in converting from the present system to the new; current volumes of data being handled by the present system, projected volumes which the new system will be expected to handle (including peak periods and other exceptional conditions), current and projected costs of the present system, and new control requirements must be determined and documented.

Data gathering is almost wholly the responsibility of the systems analyst, with assistance, in the form of providing information, from concerned user personnel.

4. System Analysis

When data gathering is completed, analysis begins. It is important to note that system analysis divides itself into two principal areas,

- analysis of data, and
- analysis of cost.

Analysis of Data   The first step, *analysis of data,* requires that the data be organized. The relationships among documents must be established, the processing flow defined, and the rules governing each step noted. It must be determined that all of the data concerned is accounted for, its source, destination, and processing known. The analyst can then define basic input and output requirements of the new system, determine which existing procedures will remain unchanged, which procedures will remain manual but with changes, and which procedures will be changed to machine processing.

Analysis of Cost   The *analysis of cost* consists of examining design alternatives to determine costs of development and installation, maintenance, and operation. Generally, attempts to reduce development costs will lead to higher maintenance and operating costs. If the system is designed initially to perform only the functions specifically required at the time of design, future requirements will cause very expensive maintenance and operating problems. If, however, attempts are made to generalize the system wherever possible, development and installation costs may be higher with compensatory savings in future maintenance and operation.

Consideration must be given to methods of reducing both development and running costs by re-evaluating the system objectives. It is frequently discovered, when costs are examined, that many functions included in the original specifications cannot be justified in terms of their worth versus their cost. This phase of system development can sometimes include an evaluation of computer equipment to do the job, and in any case, provides management with another opportunity to compare anticipated costs of the system with anticipated benefits.

This phase is wholly the responsibility of the systems analysis function; the results should be carefully reviewed by top data processing management before the next phase is allowed to begin.

5. System Design

When the analysis is complete, detailed system design begins. There are two areas of system design, file design (or data base design), which proceeds in parallel with process design (or procedure design).

Logical organization of the data is a conceptual step preceding physical design and layout. Development of the data base proceeds in three steps. First, the data requirements of the system must be identified. Data can be segmented by *purpose* into the categories of control, reporting, and supporting. It can be characterized in terms of *end use* (managerial, operational, or record-keeping), by *generic groupings,* and through *cross-indexing* and *redundancy.* Not all of these categorizations of data will apply in all cases, but they are a useful conceptual aid to the systems analyst.

Finally, physical file design can be undertaken. It must take into account the various types of files, such as single function, multi-function, quantitative, statistical, operational, transitory, archival, and historical; and file dynamics, such as file growth, retention, updating, maintenance, access, and response requirements. The restrictions placed upon the design by the requirements of file sequence and access method, record format, file medium, and processing mode must also be considered. Finally, control requirements for recovery, retention, and security are determined.

When the system design is complete, the user departments and management review the design. This is a critical stage; beyond this point in the development, changes can be very expensive. The user departments should check that the system will do correctly what is required, that the operating schedules proposed in the design are adequate to user needs, that the user can provide the clerical support called for in the design, and that the plan for system testing and conversion is adequate and feasible.

Agreement between the user departments and the data processing department on a system test plan is particularly important. If the user departments do not participate actively in the final testing of the system, including the testing of the clerical interface with the automated portions, it will be mere happenstance if the delivered system fulfills user requirements.

Only at this phase can estimates of programming installation time and cost be made. Specific procedures for estimating are given in Chapter 9.

6. Programming

Programming is the task of converting the statement of the problem, as given in the system design, into the language that the computer can understand. The term "programming" is generally taken to include the activities of specification analysis by the programmer, program logic design, coding, and desk checking. The process of specification analysis results in detailed program requirements from which the programmer can proceed. During his analysis, the programmer will record comments and questions and formulate approaches to be used to satisfy the program requirements. He should verify that all output data requirements can be met. Any suggestions for changes or improvements are noted, and these, along with any questions, can be discussed with the analyst and if necessary with the user. Any resulting changes made to the system must always be documented.

The programmer is now ready to design the program logic. The objectives of well-designed logic are, besides the obvious one of accomplishing the required processing,

- ease of coding,
- ease of testing,
- ease of operation,
- ease of maintenance, and
- the preparation of clear and concise documentation.

The design is formalized in block diagrams, decision tables, or some combination of the two. The formalized logic is then checked before the next phase of program — coding — is begun.

Coding is the process of writing the specific step-by-step instructions needed by the computer to execute the logic. To reduce the danger of incomprehensible coding, it should relate directly to the block diagrams and/or decision tables produced in the logic design phase. The coding should also contain abundant notes, comments, and remarks describing routines performed and techniques used to the accomplish the program's functions.

Because programming is a long and tedious process requiring extended concentration and attention to minute detail, errors are always present. Most can be detected and eliminated during program testing, the next phase.

7. Program Testing

A program is tested to ensure that it will work under all conditions. If *modular programming* has been used, the modules can be tested as they are completed. Modular programming is a technique in which the program is written in sections, called modules, which can be developed independently of one another, although logically interconnected.

Test cases are generally developed by the programmer, although they may also be prepared and/or checked by the systems analyst. The expected solution should always be worked out by hand in advance for comparison with the results produced by the computer.

The programmer and his manager are generally responsible for determining that all tests on a program have been completed successfully.

8. System Testing

One of the objectives of system testing is to determine that all components of the system work properly together. In this context, the components to be tested include not only the automated portions of the system, *but all human elements*. The human elements include management, clerical personnel (both for preparation of data for input to the automated processes and for utilization of the output of the automated processes), computer operations personnel, and all others who use or are affected by the system. Another objective of the systems test is to determine the validity of the system design, and to detect omissions. A system test plan must be prepared to ensure that the test will meet these objectives, and that adequate test data will be available. It is important that test data will be provided by, and the results evaluated by, user personnel at all levels, from top management to clerical personnel using the system.

Chapter 11 contains a detailed discussion of test scheduling and control.

9. Conversion and Installation

If conversion and installation are done improperly, the system will be off to a bad start in production running and will probably generate errors and cause difficulties when they can least be tolerated, i.e., during an actual run. Conversion may require that one or more computer programs be written for that purpose alone, and if so, the preparation for conversion can be considered a small system development project in itself, subject to the same control procedures and documentation requirements.

The conversion and installation may be either parallel or immediate. In parallel conversion, both the old and new systems operate side by side until the new system has successfully performed all functions in all time periods. (It is not unusual to find that a number of the apparent errors detected by this method in fact result from faults in the old system.) In an immediate conversion, the old system is discontinued at the time the new system begins operation. In this method (also known as the "guts" method), it is advisable to save data from the old system as insurance.

Another alternative is the gradual conversion, in which the old system is replaced by the new over an extended period of time, with conversion being accomplished in phases limited by selected operating cycles, major processing functions, types of data accepted, or organizations affected.

10. System Maintenance

Maintenance of systems and programs is a continuing requirement to accommodate revisions in procedures and parameters. Even if it were possible to design the "perfect" system, maintenance tasks could not be eliminated because changes in the needs of the company will require changes in its data processing systems. Just as no business remains static, neither will its information systems.

Maintenance efforts can usually be treated as short-term projects. Thus, in the project control system, the maintenance phase is not considered part of a system development project but a project in and of itself.

11. System Evaluation

After three or four full cycles of the new system, e.g., within four or five months for a system whose basic time cycle is monthly, a follow-up evaluation study should be performed. This is a function of the systems analyst, who conducts interviews, observes the system in operation, and prepares an evaluation report. The report may recommend modification to the system, if warranted, to improve

— operating efficiency,
— conformance to original specifications,
— ease of use, both for the operations and the user departments,
— operations and user documentation,
— suitability for the purpose for which it was designed, and
— conformance to standards.

The report should also include a comparison of the anticipated system benefits, as originally specified, with actual benefits to determine if the system has fulfilled requirements.

Abbreviated check-ups of all operating systems should be made at regular intervals after the initial evaluation, say, once every six months or once a year. These may take the form of questionnaires to users.

Project Checkpoints

It is now possible to define, in terms of the system development process just described, the points in a project at which there is turnover of work from one task to another. The following are checkpoints upon which project control is based:

PROJECT INITIATION
   1 Project Selection
   2 Project Authorization
   3 Project Planning
   4 Personnel Assignment
   5 Time Estimating
   6 Scheduling
   7 Budgeting
PROJECT FULFILLMENT
   8 Data Gathering— 1st Phase
   9 Data Gathering— 2nd Phase
   10 System Analysis Completion
   11 System Design— Data Base Specification
   12 System Design Completion
   13 Programming— Coding Completion
   14 Programming— Third Machine Test
   15 Programming— 75% of Program Test Budget
   16 System Test Plan Completion
   17 System Test— Intermediate Review
   18 System Test Completion
   19 Conversion and Installation Plan Completion
PROJECT COMPLETION
   20 Pre-conversion Preparation Completion
   21 Post-implementation Audit

At each checkpoint, the work performed so far is reviewed to verify that it has been completed satisfactorily and according to established standards. The next task may not be begun until

Exhibit 3: Analysis of Typical Control Points by Project Type

Control Point / Project Type	Long-term Development	Short-term Development	Maintenance (modification)	Maintenance (rescue)
Project Initiation				
1. Project Selection	X		X	
2. Project Authorization	X	X		
3. Project Planning	X			
4. Personnel Assignment	X			
5. Time Estimating	X			
6. Scheduling	X	X	X	X
7. Budgeting	X		X	
Project Fulfillment				
8. System Study	X			
9. Data Gathering	X			
10. System Analysis Completion	X			
11. System Design-Data Base Specification	X			
12. System Design Completion	X	X		
13. Programming—Coding Completion	X	X	X	
14. Programming—Third Machine Test	X	X		
15. Programming—75% of Program Test Budget	X			
	X	X	X	X
16. System Test Plan Completion	X	X	X	X
17. System Test—Intermediate Review	X			
18. System Test Completion	X	X		
19. Conversion and Installation Plan Completion	X	X		
Project Completion				
20 Pre-Conversion Preparation Completion	X	X		
21. Post-Implementation Audit	X	X	X	X

—workability,
—accuracy,
—completeness, and
—legibility

have been approved.

Of course, the actual set of tasks for any one project, the checkpoints used, and the review criteria established for each checkpoint will vary, within limits, from project to project, depending on the characteristics of the projects. Exhibit 3 gives an analysis of typical control points by project type.

In the next chapter, the events at each type of checkpoint are discussed in detail, and the control criteria given. Section II of the book is a guide to the techniques needed for good project control using the checkpoint approach.

5/ THE BASIC CONTROL ELEMENTS

The previous chapters discussed the goals of a project control system, gave the prerequisites for developing one, and outlined the checkpoint method in the context of the system development process. Implied throughout was that the elements we wish to control are the resources which are at the disposal of the data processing manager: *people, time, money,* and *equipment.* There is one further element to be controlled: *quality.*

All of the resources are theoretically variable elements. That is, in an ideal situation we could increase any one or more of them and get a corresponding (but not necessarily equal) decrease in one or more of the others. For example, by putting more people on a project we could reduce the time needed for development; or, by increasing salaries (money), obtain more skilled individuals to reduce the time element again, or vice versa; or, by spending more time, reduce the need for equipment. There are, of course, limits to how far one can successfully carry this process. And in any installation, one or more of the elements may be for practical purposes fixed. There may be only a certain amount of money available for personnel, so that the data processing manager must decide whether to spend it on four programmer trainees, or three experienced programmers, or two systems analysts. Top management may have decided that equipment upgrading has gone far enough, and to make do with what they have for the next year. Time can be stretched only so far, and the very real need to get a system operating by a certain date may take precedence over how many people are assigned to the project, and, therefore, how much money is spent on it. It is important to recognize not only what the variables are, but the practical limits to which they can be varied in a particular environment.

Quality is less easy to balance. In one sense, it is not variable at all; either the system works or it does not. But the quality of a system goes beyond that. It includes, for example, the efficiency with which the system operates, both in terms of the human effort needed to support its operation, and documentation for ease of maintenance and possible future conversion. In this light, quality control means the best possible use of the available resources: that is what project control is for.

It can be seen from the description of the system development process given earlier that user management has responsibility for quality control at many points. User management has responsibility, in some respects, for control of time and resources. In addition, the responsibility of user management extends to assuring itself that its need for quality is being met during the development of the system.

Within the data processing department, project control affects personnel at all levels. The persons working on a project have responsibility to record accurately not only the time spent on the project, but the time spent on each of the various tasks. Data processing management is responsible for control of quality, time, and resources at the various checkpoints. In the data processing department project control usually encompasses all personnel on all types of projects.

QUALITY CONTROL

Quality control procedures are designed to ensure that the system or program has been prepared according to specifications and produces the desired results, that documentation is sufficient to permit proper operation of the system, that the techniques used in the system are documented in a form which permits maintenance and additional development, and that the system uses the available machines, programming languages, and other resources efficiently.

Project Selection

At the time of *project selection* (the first checkpoint defined in Exhibit 3), an evaluation should be made of whether the proposed project or system really is suitable for automation. The automation committee (or whoever is responsible for project selection) should answer the following questions:

—Will the system really solve the user's problem?

— Is the solution a permanent one? If not, why not, and is it none-theless the best one for the moment?

— Are the benefits attributed to the project attainable by any other means?

Systems Study

At the completion of the systems study (checkpoint 8 in Exhibit 3) it is vital that data processing management evaluate the thoroughness of the study. The evaluation should answer these questions:

— Was the current environment completely explored?
— Have all the information requirements been identified?
— Are the estimated cost figures realistic?
— Have a sufficient number of design alternatives been covered?
— Did the study team review the use of all actual reports and files in the present system?
— Were user department employees consulted during the study? Are their comments and suggestions recorded or summarized?
— What additional problems were discovered?
— Has the user signed off on the study?
— Has the study resulted in any revisions to previous decisions?

System Analysis

At completion of *system analysis* (checkpoint 10 in Exhibit 3), it is important to determine that the system requirements are stated in detail and that the user groups have provided adequate personnel time for review.

Data Base Design

At the completion of *data base design* (checkpoint 11 in Exhibit 3) the systems analyst should satisfy the manager that he can answer "yes" to the following questions:

— Does the data base contain all the data required?
— Are the legitimate entries permitted for each data element fully detailed?

— Can updating techniques be developed for all elements in the data base?

— Is the user committed to collecting the data required for maintenance of the data base?

System Design

At the completion of *system design* (checkpoint 12 in Exhibit 3), the design should be checked to determine that it provides a firm basis for continuing the project. All files and procedures should be defined in detail, as should the test plan, and logic diagrams and decision tables should be complete and up to installation standards. It is important that the user also review the specifications and authorize continuance of the project based on them.

Programmer's Analysis and Coding

As the *programmer's analysis and coding* is completed (checkpoint 13 in Exhibit 3) the programming manager can perform the following quality control checks:

— Has the coding been desk-checked?

— Is the instruction use correct?

— Are sub-routines and segmentation employed properly?

— Is the program annotated adequately?

— What test cases have been used in desk-checking?

— Has a test plan been developed for each program? Does it include simple test cases to test main-line logic and reach the end of the program, cases to test each routine, each exception, end-of-file routines, combinations of parameter cards and switch settings, and cases to test unusual mixtures and sequences of data?

— Have standard language conventions been used?

— Have any tricky or unusually complicated routines been written which will require special testing? Are they adequately documented?

— Has test data been created? Does it correspond to the test plan?

Program Testing

During *program testing* (checkpoints 14 and 15 in Exhibit 3) data processing management can perform quality checks to determine that the programmer understands the machine and the problem, and as an aid in forecasting realistic completion dates.

Before system testing is begun, the *system test plan* can be checked to determine that the system will receive a thorough test (checkpoint 16 in Exhibit 3). The following questions should be answered:

- Have all programs been fully tested, ready for system testing?
- Does the system test plan cover all possibilities, including error testing and error correction procedures?
- Has provision been made to test the clerical/manual aspects of the new system as well as the automated portions?
- Is adequate test data available? How was it created? If live data is being used, has it been supplemented or altered to include all types of exceptions and errors?

During system testing (checkpoint 17 in Exhibit 3), quality control can continue with the following questions:

- How many programming changes have been required? Is there a pattern to them? What were the causes?
- Are changes in file specifications required? Why?
- Does the output from each program interface properly with succeeding programs?
- Is the system as a whole operating efficiently?

Note that here we are also checking the quality of previous work. The lessons learned can be put to good use in future projects.

Completion of System Testing

The *completion of system testing* (checkpoint 18 in Exhibit 3) is an important quality checkpoint, for it is here that the system must work in a simulation of its final product environment. Management should determine whether the test results matched the expected results, and whether the user has studied and approved the test results. If this is not the case, further work and testing are required.

The organization is ready for conversion if the programs necessary for conversion are tested, if the user has extra personnel available, and if provision has been made for controlling and documenting any changes that will be made to the system during conversion. After implementation of the system, the final quality check can be made to determine what lessons were learned that could be applied to other projects.

Checkpoint Summary

The following major checkpoints minimally should be utilized for quality control:

Project Selection   The project objectives must be clearly stated, the project properly defined, and its scope established. Some form of user request should be completed.

System Study Completion   The proposed system is reviewed with the user to determine any problem areas. Exceptions and changes in the scope of the project are identified. All documentation prepared to date is reviewed and approved (User Request, Analytical Report, Design Requirements Statement).*

System Analysis Completion   Design alternatives and system requirements are reviewed. The user approves the statement of requirements.

Data Base Design Completion   Specifications for files, transactions, outputs, and related reports are reviewed, checked against the System Summary, and discussed with and approved by the user.

System Design Completion   All System Specifications are reviewed, and additional Program Specifications are prepared, if necessary. Specifications for files, inputs, outputs, reports, controls, and processing requirements are reviewed. Readiness for programming to begin is ascertained.

Coding Completion   Logic flow specifications and the program test plan and test data are checked. Coding is reviewed to ensure that it is faithful to the logic design.

* Max Gray and Keith R. London, *Documentation Standards,* Princeton: Brandon/systems Press, 1969.

System Test Plan Completion   Upon completion of program testing, the System Test Plan is reviewed. At the same time, preliminary operating instructions are reviewed and the completion of program testing validated.

System Test — Intermediate Review   The number of program changes required, running time, program interface, errors, and test results are reviewed and checked against the System Test Plan to determine whether results are satisfactory.

System Test Completion   The results of the system test are checked against the System Specification. Changes already made and documentation changes required are reviewed, and user acceptance obtained.

Conversion and Installation Plan Completion   All user aids, including data input, output, collection, preparation and control instructions, and data processing operating instructions are reviewed. The conversion programs and procedures are checked.

Post-implementation Audit   The anticipated system benefits are compared with actual benefits to determine if the system has fulfilled requirements. Needed improvements are identified and documented.

RESOURCE CONTROL

Resource control assures the development of the desired product within the specified time using the allocated resources. This involves control of the elapsed time for project development, and the people, money, and equipment used. While some of the quality control checkpoints are appropriate as well for resource control, additional ones are needed.

Resource control is exercised on a cyclic basis during system development. The cycle has four phases, which are discussed in detail in Chapter 6. The cycle is repeated periodically throughout the development of the system.

Typical resource control points are described below.

Project Planning

In reviewing *project planning* (checkpoint 3 in Exhibit 3), data processing management and the automation committee should determine that the proper environment for continuance of the project exists by asking the following questions:

- Have future checkpoints been specified?
- Have standard task descriptions been used?
- Have review points and preparation of progress reports been included?
- Has responsibility for each task been defined?
- Is there a clear understanding of the responsibilities implied by the terms "assist," "review," "consult," "perform," and the like?
- Have separate tasks been defined for review of system and programming specifications, and for review of various test results?

Personnel Assignment

Personnel assignment (checkpoint 4) is particularly important for the data processing manager. He should answer the following questions:

- Who are the key individuals assigned to the project?
- What is the percentage of confidence that they will be available as needed?
- How would they be replaced if they became unavailable during the project? What would be the effect?
- Are sufficient back-up personnel included in the project team?
- Will the user be able to replace personnel assigned to the project, if needed?
- If training is required, when and how will it be done?

System Design Completion

System Design completion (checkpoint 12) is excellent for estimating the required programming manpower and time. The following questions should be answered:

- Has a detailed task list been constructed?
- Are standards available for each task?
- If standards were not used, what technique was used for estimating?

— If separate independent estimates were made, what degree of compromise does the final estimate contain?

— How does this estimate compare to similar completed projects?

Similar questions should be answered at each resource control point.

Estimating and scheduling are covered in more detail in the next section. In general, they are iterative processes; that is, a review should be made of the estimates and schedules for the next phases of the project at each checkpoint, and previous estimates revised as needed.

Budgeting is usually not as flexible, since in most companies it is not entirely at the option of the data processing manager. Budgets should take into account all costs, including user costs and the costs of idle time caused by delays. Detailed estimates should be available to back up each budgeted amount. In designing the project control system, appropriate budget checkpoints should be built in, conforming to previously established company policy and procedures.

Other time and resource control points, which have been discussed more fully under quality control, are the times of completion of the system study, system analysis, system design, coding, at various times during program testing, at the completion of the system test plan, and during system testing.

The final checkpoint for time and resources is the same as that for quality control, and attempts to answer the same question, namely, "What lessons were learned that can be applied to other projects?"

Checkpoint Summary

In summary, the following checkpoints are those most important for resource control:

Project Authorization   When the user and data processing are ready to proceed with the project, the objectives are reviewed and accepted.

Project Planning   The project plan includes a detailed task outline and an analysis of required skills.

Personnel Assignment   The personnel required for the project are assigned in this phase.

Time Estimating Analytical documentation and the list of project tasks are reviewed in detail, and standards are applied for the estimation of time required to complete the project. As with previous tasks, these will be reviewed and adjusted at future checkpoints.

Scheduling Task estimates are reviewed to develop a total project schedule. The schedule must be reviewed and adjusted at future checkpoints.

Budgeting Tasks and time are listed; standard rates are applied to develop a complete picture of project costs. Usually, the budget will be reviewed by the automation committee and/or top management, and a decision made. Again, budgets must be reviewed throughout the project.

The objectives of the checkpoints in the project fulfillment and project conclusion phases have been given under quality control. In general, progress should be compared against the prepared schedule at each, and revisions made as needed. The major checkpoints are:

System Study Completion
System Analysis Completion
System Design Completion
Coding Completion
First Stage of Program Testing
Final Stage of Program Testing
System Test Plan Completion
System Test — Intermediate Review
Post-implementation Audit

6/ THE PROJECT CONTROL SYSTEM

The most important objective of a project control system is to focus attention on problems *in time for management to do something about them*. Problems may arise in the use of any of the resources — people, time, money, and equipment — or in the quality of the product produced. The use of checkpoints to control quality has been discussed and will be discussed further in later chapters. In this chapter we will be concerned with the mechanism for providing management with the information it needs to control people, time, money, and equipment.

It is important to distinguish control information from after-the-fact accounting information. Accounting information may be useful for billing customers, setting standard costs, and for future projects. Control information, on the other hand, must

- indicate that a problem has developed or is likely to develop,
- provide indications of the cause of the problem and of likely remedies,
- be presented so as to enable management to direct its attention to those areas requiring it, and to ignore other areas, and
- be presented in time for corrective action to be taken.

Other objectives of a project control system, as mentioned in Chapter 2, include the ability to predict future resource needs and to plan for remaining portions of a project, and to evaluate personnel performance.

This chapter presents an example of a project control mechanism that meets all of these objectives. The example is based on a software system developed by Brandon Applied Systems, Inc. The system is called Project Control System (PCS), and is one of two subsystems of the Resource Management System (RMS). But before looking at PCS, let us examine the steps of the project control cycle.

THE PROJECT CONTROL CYCLE

This section describes the functions which must be performed by any project control system. Here we are concerned with the entire system, including both clerical and managerial functions. The clerical functions can be (and, in **PCS**, are) performed by a computer, but management action *must be performed by management.*

The functions of project control are carried out by relying on certain pieces of information — inputs, reports, etc. — which we shall call elements. Figure 1 shows the functions of project control, and their relationships to the elements of project control and to each other. The functions of project control are shown in rectangles and the elements on which the project control cycle depends are shown in circles.

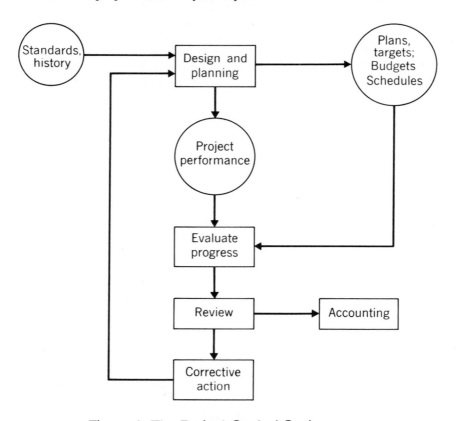

Figure 1: The Project Control Cycle

Design and Planning

Planning for a project is a vital function in project control. Without planning there can be no control. Usually, planning should be carried down to a level of detail that will allow the kind of control desired. Later we will see how PCS aids in planning at the correct level of detail. For our purposes, planning consists of four related activities, each of which has a definable output. The four outputs constitute the plan for the project. The four activities are:

Estimating   The purpose of estimating, in the present context, is to determine how many man- and machine-hours will be required for execution of the project, as well as the quantities of other consumable resources that will be needed. In system development projects, we are interested also in estimating the number of accesses to the computer that will be required as part of program testing, and computer accesses may be treated as a resource. In other types of projects, other resources may have to be estimated.

Estimating may be done in several ways. PCS uses a combination of standards and historical data, in a manner which will be described later, to produce estimates which reflect both desirable and actual conditions.

Budgeting   The purpose of budgeting is to estimate the dollar costs of the resources to be used in the project. Budgets can of course be used for purposes outside of project control, for example, as part of the economic justification for a project, but we will deal with the use of budgets as tools for project control.

Scheduling   Whereas estimating determines how much of various resources will be consumed in the execution of a project, scheduling determines how long tasks are to take and when they are to be performed.

Scheduling can be done in many ways. In scheduling a systems development project, it is important to recognize the interdependence of tasks, and to schedule accordingly. Most systems development projects are of small to moderate size, and formal networking is not needed. In larger projects, networks (such as are used in PERT or CPM) may be needed in order to account for all task interdependencies. PCS permits the user to use any scheduling method desired.

Resource Allocation   The purpose of resource allocation is to assign, or commit, specific resources to project tasks. In systems development, resources consist of men and computers. Since assignment of men is made on the basis of an individual's skills and availability, the assignment to a task implies a commitment of that individual to the task. Likewise, computers (or computer time) should be committed to tasks as part of the planning for a project.

The Project Plan

The documentation produced by the four activities of estimating, budgeting, scheduling, and resource allocation constitute the *project plan*. Such a plan is usually developed by first-line project management and reviewed by higher levels of management. The plan can serve several purposes before work on the project is begun. It can, for example, enable upper management to determine whether it wishes to change the scope of the project, or change the elapsed time by altering resource commitments. The plan may thus be revised before project work is begun, but at some point the plan is accepted by all concerned, and project performance begins. It is then that the plan is used for control purposes, as part of progress evaluation.

Progress Evaluation and Review

In order for management to evaluate project progress, it is not enough to know where the project stands at any time. It is also necessary to know where the project *should* stand. The goal of every project control system must be to provide management with a reliable method of comparing actual progress to the plan. That is, a project control system should provide genuine control information, as defined in the introduction to this chapter, so that

- deviations from plan are recognized as soon as they occur,
- possible deviations from plan are recognized as soon as the possibility of deviation arises,
- management can completely ignore those aspects of projects which are proceeding according to plan,
- attention can be directed only to those aspects of projects which are deviating from the plan, and
- some indication of the possible cause of deviation is given.

PCS develops and presents its project progress information so that all of the above characteristics are present.

Since the plan consists of various elements — namely estimates and budgets of various kinds of resources, and schedules — it is possible to compare elements of progress to corresponding elements of the plan. That is, actual man-time expenditure should be compared to the planned man-time expenditure, actual machine-time expenditure to the planned machine-time expenditure, etc. Also, actual progress on tasks should be compared to scheduled progress.

In systems development projects, a particularly valuable resource is computer accesses. The use of the computer by programmers should be planned on a test-by-test basis, and a project control system should provide some way of comparing actual computer usage to the planned usage. This control of computer usage is in addition to the control of computer time mentioned earlier. PCS provides comparisons on all these elements of plan and progress, and helps to point out what kind of corrective action is needed, and where.

It is the responsibility of persons working on a project to submit progress information periodically to the project control system. The form that such information might take is discussed later in this chapter. The control system then presents comparisons of progress and plan to first-line project management for evaluation and review. Higher levels of management might also want less detailed comparisons of progress with plan.

Corrective Action

Evaluation and review of project progress to date may indicate a need for management to take corrective action. Sometimes, when progress is deviating from the plan, it is sufficient to correct the source (usually human) of the deviation. This may consist of correcting difficulties that a particular programmer may be having, or it may involve reducing computer downtime or getting higher priority for testing, or getting improved user commitment, etc. In any case, the purpose of this kind of corrective action is to get the project back onto the plan.

Usually, however, it is not possible to get the project back onto the plan, and replanning is required. The replanning might at the least involve changing estimates of man-time but not schedules. In more serious cases of deviations from plan, the schedules may have to be changed as well. A project control system should aid management in the decisions which must be made in order for corrective action to be taken. PCS provides such aid in several ways, which will be discussed later. In Figure 1 it can be seen that the evaluation and review of progress leads to corrective action, which may in turn lead to replanning. Subsequent progress evaluation should compare progress against the new plan. The original plan should be ignored for purposes of progress evaluation, although the original plan may be useful for other purposes, such as evaluating the planners.

Continued execution of the project control cycle leads eventually to the conclusion of the project. Information accumulated during the life of the project is available for accounting, for updating of standards, and for historical purposes.

Accounting

Since budgets and dollar expenditures constitute some of the information needed for control, any project control system will be able to provide some after-the-fact accounting information based on monetary control data. The forms in which accounting information is presented, and the degree of detail obtained, will of course vary from system to system. It may be desirable in some cases to segregate accounting information according to labor categories, or customer categories, or according to organizational lines.

PCS presents all of its after-the-fact accounting information organized by project. Provision is made for more specialized use of the accounting data by individual users.

TYPICAL CONTROL SYSTEM

Now that the required steps in a project control cycle have been defined, let us examine a working project control system to see how it carries out its clerical project control functions, and delivers the information needed in order that management may carry out its managerial project control functions. The project control system to be examined is Brandon Applied Systems' PCS, a subsystem of RMS.

RMS is composed of two subsystems: Operations Control System (OCS) and Project Control System (PCS). The purpose of OCS is to aid operations management by automating the three principal operations functions — equipment scheduling, tape and disk library control, and machine utilization and analytical reporting. The purpose of PCS is to forecast, record, and control resources in a multi-project environment. The system maintains estimates, time and cost history, and utilization records on all levels of project activity.

Project Planning

1. Estimates and Budgets   The user may request PCS to perform estimating and budgeting several times during the life of a project. Before a project begins, the user may want rough estimates. Later, he may want firm estimates on early project tasks, and after those tasks are completed he may want firm estimates on tasks which occur later in the project, such as programming and testing. PCS estimates on the basis of standards, using some of the techniques for estimating described in Chapter 9. To request estimates and budgets from PCS, the user must provide only the following information:

— The type of project being estimated,
— A descriptor of the difficulty of each task, group of tasks, phase, or group of phases to be estimated.

The user can provide descriptors at any desired level of detail. Early in the project, phase descriptors may be most practical; later in the project it becomes necessary to estimate and budget by task. A segment of a sample Estimates and Budgets Report is given in Figure 2, showing task estimates for Phases G19 and H01.

2. Resource Requirements Forecast   After estimates have been reviewed by management, and modified if necessary, management is in a position to do preliminary scheduling and resource allocation. The Resource Requirements Forecast is compiled by PCS to indicate how the proposed use of resources compares to resources available in the installation.

To obtain a Resource Requirements Forecast, the user must provide PCS with his resource requirements by type of resource for several time periods. PCS then refers to its Resource File and its On-going Projects File to determine total installation resources and committed resources.

The Forecast enables management to determine whether any or all proposed projects can be executed in the proposed time frame. On the basis of the Forecast, management can

Figure 2: RMS—Project Control System
Estimates and Budgets

PROJECT NO.—LTD4A   TYPE—LD   DESCRIPTION—ACCOUNTS RECEIVABLE SYSTEM

MANAGER

PHASE NO.	TASK NO.	DESCRIPTION	DESCRIPTOR	RESOURCE	HOURS	COMPUTER	BUDGET	TOTAL
G19	A01	REVIEW SPECIFICATIONS	B2	PROGRAMMER	4.00		$ 20	$ 20
	B01	LOGIC DESIGN AND BLOCK DIAGRAMMING	B2	PROGRAMMER	8.00		40	40
	C01	CODING	B2	PROGRAMMER	10.00		50	50
	D01	DESK CHECKING	B2	PROGRAMMER	4.00		20	20
	E01	PREPARE TEST DATA	B2	PROGRAMMER	6.00		30	30
	F01	PROGRAM TESTING	B2	PROGRAMMER	30.00		150	
		8.00 016 400 550						
	G01	INTEGRATED PROGRAM TESTING	B2	PROGRAMMER	5.00		25	
				360/40	3.00	003	150	175
	H01	PROGRAM DOCUMENTATION	B2	PROGRAMMER	4.00		20	20
		PHASE TOTAL		PERSONNEL	71.00		355	
				360/40	11.00	019	550	
60/40		PHASE TYPE TOTAL		PERSONNEL	1414.00		7,070	
				360/40	226.00	379	11,300	18,370
H01	A01	TRAINING IN USE OF INPUTS	B5	SYS ANLST	2.00		20	20
	B01	TRAINING IN USE OF OUTPUTS	B6	SYS ANLST	2.00		20	20
	C01	ERROR HANDLING	D2	SYS ANLST	4.00		40	40
	D01	TEST CASE PREPARATION	C5	SYS ANLST	3.00		30	30
	E01	USER MANAGEMENT TRAINING	C3	SYS ANLST	2.00		20	20
		PHASE TOTAL		PERSONNEL	13.00		130	130

— Reschedule a proposed project,
— Plan to use different resources,
— Change the scope of the proposed project, and obtain new estimates and budgets,
— Consider changing the number of resources in the installation,
— Consider rescheduling existing projects, and/or
— Change project priorities.

Any of the above changes may require the production of new estimates and budgets and a new Resource Requirements Forecast. Either of these can be produced by PCS as often as desired until a satisfactory use of resources is obtained. The segment of the Resource Requirements Forecast, shown in Figure 3, describes the availability and commitments of systems analysts and programmers. For each of the two resource types, their commitments to current projects and their proposed use on proposed projects are shown. The commitments and requirements are shown as average monthly figures for the six months starting from the present, the seventh through twelfth months, and the twelfth through seventeenth months. The total availability of resources in the installation is compared to the amounts committed to on-going projects and to the amounts proposed for new projects.

3. Assigning Schedules and Resources to Tasks Once preliminary planning indicates that a project is feasible and desirable, it is necessary to finalize the plan by assigning a schedule and resources to each task. In PCS, a task schedule consists of a start date and a completion date.

Schedules can be determined in any manner desired by management. PCS does not require that networking or any other specific method be used. Any part of the project, or the complete project, may be scheduled at any time, and any part of the schedule may be changed at any time. This feature permits management to schedule only the early tasks of a project before execution of the project begins, and to schedule the remaining tasks later. Likewise, PCS may be informed of resource assignments at any time, and the resource assignments may be changed as often as needed.

No report is produced as a result of the assignment of schedules and resources to tasks. Schedule and resource information is added to the On-going Projects File and shows on the Project Progress Report, which is produced by PCS weekly. The plan for the project is now complete, and execution of the project may begin.

Figure 3: RMS–Project Control System Resource Requirements Forecast

DATE PRODUCED 03/12/70
EFFECTIVE DATE 03/09/70
USER NO.–R2

RESOURCE TYPE	PROJECT NO.	AVERAGE MONTHLY REQUIREMENTS		
		CURRENT 6 MOS.	NEXT 6 MOS.	BEYOND 12 MOS.
SYS ANLYST	NCL2-B	30	0	0
	KVB3-F	60	30	0
	GHN7-C	60	30	0
TOTAL REQUIREMENTS FOR ON-GOING PROJECTS		150*	60*	0*
	LTD4-A	180	120	30
	STD5-C	240	240	180
TOTAL REQUIREMENTS FOR PROPOSED PROJECTS		420*	360*	210*
TOTAL AVAILABILITY		400**	400-*	360**
AVAILABLE FOR PROPOSED PROJECTS		250**	340-**	360**
EXCESS OR DEFICIENCY		170-*	20-*	150**
PRGMR /40	NCL2-B	300	300	100
	KVB3-F	120	60	0
	GHN7-C	120	60	0
TOTAL REQUIREMENTS FOR ON-GOING PROJECTS		540*	420*	100*
	LTD4-A	0	60	300
	STD5-C	0	0	120
TOTAL REQUIREMENTS FOR PROPOSED PROJECTS		0*	60*	420*
TOTAL AVAILABILITY		600**	500**	400**
AVAILABLE FOR PROPOSED PROJECTS		60-*	80**	300**
EXCESS OR DEFICIENCY		60-*	20-*	120-*

Project Fulfillment

Once a project is underway, the project fulfillment section of PCS requires the periodic input from employees working on the project. The section also produces periodic reports.

1. Time Reporting   In each time period, which may be a week or any other desired period, each employee reports on the tasks on which he has worked during the period. The information required for each task is

- Project number,
- Phase number,
- Task number,
- Hours worked,
- Hours of computer time used,
- Number of computer accesses used (this datum and the previous one can be obtained from OCS, if that type of system is installed),
- Estimated number of man-hours to complete task, and
- Estimated number of computer accesses to complete.

The estimated values are employee-generated. This is the only information required on a regular basis by PCS. If recorded daily and submitted weekly, it takes very little time to prepare. By referring to the Resource File and the On-going Projects File, PCS validates the information submitted by employees. It also checks that each employee has submitted charges for a specified minimum number of hours.

2. Project Progress Reports   By using the reported time information and the On-going Projects File, PCS produces two weekly project progress reports, the detailed report (Figure 4) is intended for first-level project management and the summary report (Figure 5) for higher management. It is assumed that the project manager is interested in detailed task information and the next level of management is interested in over-all financial information.

Both reports attempt to show, in a form that is easy for management to use, how the current state of the project compares to the plan. That is, the reports show what the planned progress to date is, and compares that to actual progress. Flags are used so that management may direct its attention to those aspects of progress which are deviating from the plan, and ignore those aspects which are in accordance with

Figure 4: RMS-Project Control System
Detailed Project Progress Report

DATE PRODUCED 05/06/70
PERIOD COVERED 04/26/70–05/02/70
USER NO.–R2

PROJECT NO.–LTD4-A   TYPE–LD   DESCRIPTION–ACCOUNTS RECEIVABLE SYSTEM
PHASE NO.–G19   TYPE–FILE LISTING AND REORGANIZATION
TASK NO.–A01   DESCRIPTOR–B2   DESCRIPTION–REVIEW SPECIFICATIONS

MANAGER
PROGRAM NO. LTD19AID

RESOURCE IDENTIFICATION	ESTIMATES HOURS	COMPUTER ACCESSES	–HOURS USED– THIS PERIOD	TO DATE	PRECENT COMPLETE	NEW TOTAL EST PERIOD ENDING 4/25	PERIOD ENDING 5/02	COMPLETION DATES SCHED	PROJECTED	VARIANCE	COMPUTER ACCESSES THIS PERIOD	ACCESSES TO DATE	AVERAGE TIME PER TEST	FLAGS
W HOWARD	4.00		4.00		100	4.00	4.00	5/02	5/02	5/02				
TASK NO. –B01 DESCRIPTOR–B2 DESCRIPTION–LOGIC DESIGN AND BLOCK DIAGRAMMING											PROGRAM NO. LTD19AID			EI
W HOWARD	10.00		12.00		100	10.00	12.00	5/02	5/02	4.00				
TASK NO. –C01 DESCRIPTOR–B2 DESCRIPTION–CODING											PROGRAM NO. LTD19AID			EBI
W HOWARD	10.00		6.00	9.00	60	10.00	15.00	5/02	5/03	5.00	PROGRAM NO. LTD19AID			
TASK NO. –D01 DESCRIPTOR–B2 DESCRIPTION–DESK CHECKING														A
W HOWARD	4.00				0	4.00	4.00	5/09	5/08					

PHASE TOTALS

	ESTIMATES HOURS	COMPUTER ACCESSES	–HOURS USED– THIS PERIOD	TO DATE	PRECENT COMPLETE	NEW TOTAL EST PERIOD ENDING 4/25	PERIOD ENDING 5/02	COMPLETION DATES SCHED	PROJECTED	VARIANCE	FLAGS
PERSONNEL	76.00 $380		6.00 $30	25.00 $125	31	79.00 $395	90.00 $450	6/12	6/12	14.00 $280	EI
360/40	11.00 $550	019		11.00 $550		11.00 $550					

Figure 5: RMS—Project Control System
Project Progress Report
Summary

DATE PRODUCED 05/06/70
PERIOD COVERED 04/26/70—05/02/70
USER NO.—R2

LTD4-A   DESCRIPTION—ACCOUNTS RECEIVABLE SYSTEM   MANAGER

(SUB) PROJECT NUMBER	BUDGET ORIGINAL	BUDGET LATEST	EXPENDED THIS PERIOD	EXPENDED PROJECT TO DATE	EXPENDED YEAR TO DATE	PERCENT OF BUDGET UTILIZED	PERCENT COMPLETE	COMPLETION DATES SCHED	COMPLETION DATES PROJECTED	PROJECTED TOTAL PERIOD ENDING 4/25	PROJECTED TOTAL PERIOD ENDING 5/02	PROJECTED VARIANCE	FLAGS
PERSONNEL	$14,300	$18,000	$1,680	$5,220	$4,080	29	32	6/26	6/26	$15,900	$16,300	$1,700	CR
EQUIPMENT	2,320	2,320	150	450	450	19	14			2,960	3,150	830	E
TRAVEL	1,000	1,000		600	532	53				1,000	1,000		
SUB-PROJ	$17,620	$21,320	$1,830	$6,270	$5,062	24				$19,860			
TOTALS								6/26	6/26		$20,450	870	CR

the plan. In this way no management time is wasted on items needing no management attention. In addition, the flags enable management to read through the report very quickly, looking only for those items which are flagged, and hence in need of corrective action. Unflagged items may be ignored by management, for they are adhering to the plan in every respect. An item is flagged as soon as it becomes likely that the estimate will be exceeded or the schedule missed, or for other reasons.

3. Resource Inventory by Man   This report is produced weekly from the same information used to produce the project progress reports. It reports, by man, on all project and non-project time spent during the week.

The segment of the Resource Inventory shown here (Figure 6) reports the activities of one person.

4. Test Schedule and Control   This is a special feature of PCS which permits management to have control over the way the computer is used in development projects. Before program testing is scheduled to begin in a project, the Test Schedule and Control documents should be requested from PCS. These include individual program test plans for each program in the system and a schedule of all planned program testing.

For each program to be tested, PCS produces a set of sequentially numbered test plans. The number of test plans in the set is equal to the estimated number of computer accesses for that program. The programmer is expected to submit one test plan to operations each time he uses the computer, to note on his test plan what is to be tested, and, when the plan is returned to him, the results of the test. This furnishes management with a permanent record of how the computer was used. If the programmer uses up all his test plan forms and needs more, he may request them through his manager who may then change the estimate of the number of computer accesses and have PCS produce additional test plan forms. Management thus has positive control over the use of the computer. A sample test plan is shown in Figure 8. The Testing Schedule and Control lists all programs for which testing schedules have been established, the estimated number of computer accesses for each, and the scheduled start and finish dates for testing of each. Management can then see what priorities must be assigned to tests in order that the estimated number of tests be accomplished in the desired time.

Figure 6: RMS–Project Control System
Resource Inventory
By Man Number

DATE PRODUCED 05/06/70
EFFECTIVE DATE 05/02/70
USER NO.–R2

EMPLOYEE IDENT AND RESOURCE TYPE	PROJECT NUMBER	PHASE NO.	TASK	THIS PERIOD EXPENDITURE			REMAINING EXPENDITURE		COMMITMENT LEVEL	PROJECTED COMPLETION DATE	VARIANCE	
				HOURS REG	O/T	DOLLARS	HRS	DOLLARS			HRS	DOLLARS
W Howard	LTD4-A	G19	C01	6.00		$30	6.00	$30	7.50	5/03/70	5.00	$25
Pgmr /40	LTD4-B	H01	A01	9.00		45	40.00	200	15.00	5/20/70	10.00-	50-
	LTD4-C	H01	A01	7.50	1.50	53	15.00	75	15.00	5/10/70		
Project Sub-Total				22.50	1.50	$128	61.00	$305	37.50		5.00-	$25-
Hol				7.50		38						
Sick				7.50		38						
Non-Project Sub-Total				15.00		$76						
Total				37.50	1.50	$204	61.00	$305	37.50		5.00-	$25-

NON-PROJECT SUMMARY BY TYPE

NON-PROJECT TYPE	THIS PERIOD		YEAR TO DATE	
	HOURS	DOLLARS	HOURS	DOLLARS
Vac	38	$228	75	$450
Hol	225	1,350	675	4,050
Sick	23	138	450	2,700
Trng	8	32	140	520
Misc			60	360
Total	294	$1,718	1400	$8,080

Figure 7: RMS—Project Control System Program Test Plan Program

DATE PRODUCED 4/11/70   PROGRAM NO.—LTD19AID
PROJECT NO.—LTD4-A
TEST PLAN NO.—012

403

*ERROR—ILLEGAL TYPE CODE MUST BE 1 OR 2

1. TEST THE FOLLOWING CASES

2. TEST PROCEDURE

3. CONDITION OF TEST FAILURE

4. TEST RESULTS ANALYSIS
   TYPE OF ERROR   LOGIC
                    CLERICAL
                    KEYPUNCH
                    OPERATIONS
                    SYSTEMS ANALYSIS
                    OTHER

Figure 8: RMS—Project Control System
Testing Schedule and Control

DATE PRODUCED 4/11/70

USER NO.—R2
PROJECT NO.—LTD4-A   TYPE—LD   DESCRIPTION—ACCOUNTS RECEIVABLE SYSTEM   MANAGER

PROGRAM NUMBER	DESCRIPTOR	COMPUTER ACCESSES	SCHEDULED TESTING DATES START	COMPLETE	PRIORITY	AUTHORIZATION LEVEL
LTD01AID	A1	008	4/25/70	5/02/70		
LTD01BID	A2	012	4/25/70	5/02/70		
LTD02SID	A1	008	4/25/70	5/02/70		
LTD04AID	C5	024	4/25/70	5/09/70		
LTD06AID	D4	025	4/25/70	5/09/70		
LTD09AID	B1	012	5/02/70	5/16/70		
LTD19AID	B2	019	5/02/70	5/16/70		
TOTAL FOR PROJECT		108				

The columns Priority and Authorization Level are provided for use by management. Authorization Level refers to the management level at which a person must report back to management on his progress.

5. Plan Alterations   During project fulfillment, corrective action may require modifications to man- or machine-time estimates, budgets, and/or estimates of the number of computer accesses. PCS permits such modifications to be made easily. The modified figures are recorded in the On-going Projects File as "latest estimate" or "latest budget," as the case may be. The first estimates and budgets recorded in the file are called "original estimates" and "original budgets."

It may be necessary to alter schedule dates also. In this case, "original start dates" and "original completion dates" would be superseded by "latest start dates" and "latest completion dates." These latest start dates should not be confused with the latest dates in networking; in PCS, "latest date" means only the most recently scheduled date.

Only the latest estimates, budgets, and schedules show on the detailed project progress report. Only the original estimates and budgets show on the project completion report.

Project Completion: Project Completion Report

The project fulfillment cycle continues until management determines that a project is complete. Then, on request, PCS produces a Project Completion Report. At the same time, the project is removed from the On-going Projects File and placed on the Project History File. Projects can later be purged from the history file on request.

The Project Completion Report compares original estimates and budgets to actual time and money spent. A segment of a Project Completion Report is given in Figure 9, showing original estimated Hours, Computer Accesses, and Budgets for each task, and the actual expended amounts. The actual completion information is used to update the task standards as soon as the task is completed.

Summary

We have now seen how PCS aids management in project planning, project fulfillment, and in project completion reporting. The reports

Figure 9: RMS-Project Control System Project Completion Report

DATE PRODUCED 7/05/70

USER NO.-R2

PROJECT NO.-LTD4-A   TYPE-LD   DESCRIPTION-ACCOUNTS RECEIVABLE SYSTEM   MANAGER
PHASE NO.-G19   DESCRIPTION-FILE LISTING AND REORGANIZATION

RESOURCE IDENTIFICATION	-- ESTIMATES -- HOURS	COMPUTER ACCESSES	BUDGET	-- EXPENDED -- HOURS	COMPUTER ACCESSES	BUDGET	
TASK NO. -A01			DESCRIPTOR-B2 $20	4.00		DESCRIPTION-REVIEW SPECIFICATIONS $20	PROGRAM NO. LTD19AID
W HOWARD 4.00							
TASK NO. -B01			DESCRIPTOR-B2 $45	12.00		DESCRIPTION-LOGIC DESIGN AND BLOCK DIAGRAMMING $60	PROGRAM NO. LTD19AID
W HOWARD 9.00							
TASK NO. -C01			DESCRIPTOR-B2 $50	18.00		DESCRIPTION-CODING $90	PROGRAM NO. LTD19AID
W HOWARD 10.00							
TASK NO. -D01			DESCRIPTOR-B2 $20	3.50		DESCRIPTION-DESK CHECKING $18	PROGRAM NO. LTD19AID
W HOWARD 4.00							

PHASE TOTALS

	HOURS	COMPUTER ACCESSES	BUDGET	HOURS	COMPUTER ACCESSES	BUDGET
PERSONNEL	72.00	19	$360	98.00	26	$490
360/40	11.00		$550	12.50		$625

provided by PCS direct management's attention to those areas needing attention, and the flexibility provided by PCS for changing of plans causes the project to be always under management control.

SECTION 2

PROCEDURES

In this section we present a variety of procedures and techniques which will be needed by the data processing manager in administering a project control system. They are:

Application Identification and Project Selection   The all-important tasks of recognizing what problems need to be solved and choosing applications for automation.

The Priority System   Priorities are a method for establishing and controlling the relative importance of on-going and pending system development work.

Time Estimating and Project Planning   Time estimating and project planning are one of the historically weakest areas of project control. Standards are applied to estimate the time needed to complete each task in system development.

Personnel Assignment   When time estimates have been developed, personnel are assigned. This is also a danger area for the manager.

Scheduling   Scheduling is the technique of fitting tasks to be accomplished to an over-all time scheme to develop a total project timetable.

Progress Reporting   Reporting on progress is a function of every member of the project team. Reports are used to refine and adjust estimates and the schedule for remaining portions of the project.

Review and Progress Analysis   The data processing manager must analyze progress reports and make decisions about needed corrective action.

Cost Allocation   The costs of systems development are recorded and analyzed by type of resource expended.

Most documents referenced in this section are shown as exhibits in Section 3: "Documentation."

7/ APPLICATION IDENTIFICATION AND PROJECT SELECTION

Inadequate preparation for beginning the project is a problem distinct from inadequate problem or system definition, although the two are closely related. Inadequate systems definition is usually the result of incomplete data base specification, inadequate comprehension of exception requirements, and the like. On the other hand, inadequate application definition normally results from a failure of the user and the research and development functions of the data processing department to agree on the objectives of the project, the scope of the project, and level of resources (including management talent) to be committed to the project, both by the user department and the data processing department.

For example, failure of the management of data processing and management of the user group to agree, at the very beginning, on the exact functions of the user department which are to be included in the project can result in a tremendous waste of time and money. In some cases, it is not discovered until the system design has been completed. In the worst cases, where there is .poor communication between the two groups, it is not discovered until the system is on the air that the system is not doing what user management thought it was going to do. The exact scope of the new system must be defined, documented, and understood by all before work proceeds.

The process of application identification and project selection thus becomes the foundation upon which effective project management control should be based.

The User Request

The first step is mutual recognition of the type of project being contemplated. The *User Request* is the key document in the project selection process. In some organizations, it may be called the Work Request, Pending Project Request, or the like. It may not actually always be prepared by user management, but by data processing staff or even top corporate management. However, some type of initial request form specifying what is desired must be prepared as the first step.

Where new system development is indicated, the basic question to be asked is how deeply the application area must be penetrated:

— Will an existing system be simply upgraded to faster equipment?
— Will present forms and reports be continued?
— Are any procedural questions subject to review and change?
— Are management's methods, habits, and practices subject to review, appraisal, and change?

Consideration of these and similar matters helps answer the question of what is to be included and what is to be deferred for subsequent action.

The committee selecting or authorizing the project must have sufficient authority to approve the level of expenditure required and must also have the authority to compel both data processing and user personnel to comply with project standards.

Certain preliminary estimates must be provided. The uncertainty inherent in estimates at this stage of system development must be kept in mind, however, in reaching a decision either to approve the total project or to approve the project in stages subsequent to the development of firm estimates. The latter course is recommended.

The steps in project selection are outlined in the flowchart in Exhibit 4.

New ideas for EDP projects can originate from any of the various departments or branches. The User Request is used for documenting the idea. The individual completing the form merely has to describe, in non-technical terms, the service he is requesting and the general anticipated benefits.

The User Request is then sent to the manager of research and development, the data processing manager, or someone of comparable responsibility, who will review it for over-all feasibility. If clarification is required, he may return the form to the originator with specific questions to be answered. In most cases he will probably want to meet personally with the originator to discuss the request in more detail. If

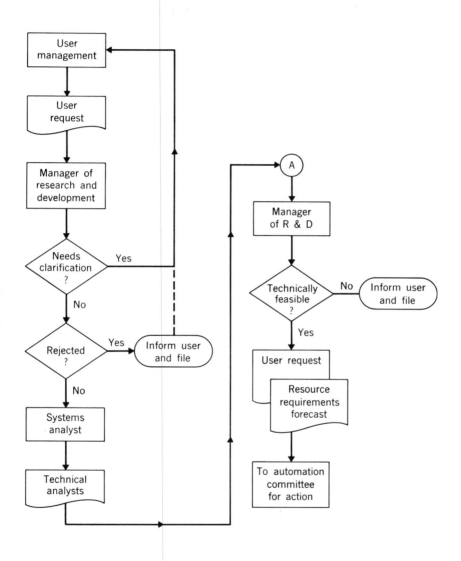

Exhibit 4: Application Identification and Project Selection

the request is rejected at this stage, the form is filed and the requestor is informed of the action.

If the manager who has reviewed the request thinks that it has some merit, he forwards it with his comments to a member of the data processing department for technical analysis. The systems analyst is usually a senior systems person, if possible one who has some previous experience with or knowledge of the general application area. He makes comments on the technical feasibility of the idea, and makes a rough, preliminary estimate of the systems, programming, and operator mandays that might be required, and of the computer time that might be required to implement the request.

The User Request is then returned to the manager, who will once again evaluate the request in the light of the added technical analysis.

The Resource Requirements Forecast

In order to provide the automation committee with the necessary data to approve and schedule projects, the data processing manager should prepare the Resource Requirements Forecast (an example of which is given in the section on documentation). It contains estimates of the manpower and equipment requirements for on-going projects or applications, and for approved pending projects. The manager has three sources of information to aid in preparing the forecast:

1. *The Pending Projects File*, which contains copies of approved User Requests, including the estimates for manpower and equipment requirements for approved pending projects.

2. *Progress Reports* (discussed in detail in Chapter 12), which give detailed estimates of manpower and equipment required to complete active development projects.

3. *Monthly Operator Time and Equipment Usage Reports* (examples of which are given in Chapter 17), which contain the monthly hours of use of operator time and equipment for implemented 'live' aplications.

Time reported as man-hours in these documents should be converted to man-days for use in the Resource Requirements Forecast. All resource requirements should be divided into three time periods: current six months (next and the succeeding five months), subsequent six months, and all projects which will not be completed within the next twelve months.

The Resource Requirements Forecast should be prepared once a month, more often if significant changes in resource forecasts are being made for consideration of the automation committee.

The Forecast is then used by the automation committee to review present capacity to complete current projects and to start new projects. On the basis of a one-year forecast, required machine and personnel time can be allowed by scheduling present capacity or, if necessary, by acquiring additional manpower and equipment. New projects are approved and given starting and completion dates, pending projects are reassigned priorities, and requisitions for equipment and personnel are generated.

In many companies, longer range forecasts may be needed. This is particularly true if the company and/or the data processing department are expanding at a rapid rate, and there are a large number of pending projects. Two, three, or even five-year plans may be necessary. In any case, they are prepared by the data processing manager and reviewed by the automation committee in a similar manner.

In summary, careful planning, documentation of future resource requirements, and a formal procedure for initiating development requests will provide a sound project identification and selection procedure on which to build the project control system.

8/ THE PRIORITY SYSTEM

If the implementation of systems is to proceed in an orderly manner —
one of the implied goals of a project control system — there must be
some method of determining the relative importance of each automation project to the business and to all other projects competing for the
resources of the data processing department. Further, there is a need
for a recognized, objective rating for each project that governs the
level of resources committed to it throughout the development process,
again in relation to all other projects under development. A priority
classification system gives us this method.

At the time the automation committee authorizes a project on the
basis of the User Request and the Resource Requirements Forecast, it
should assign a priority. This should be done before any other work on
the project is performed. The committee may take the recommendation
of the data processing manager and of the concerned user department,
but the final decision should be made in an objective manner by the
committee.

The basic priority scheme recommended here has been successfully used in many installations. While minor modifications may be
made to it to suit individual needs, the over-all plan is quite workable in
all types of businesses.

All candidate projects can be given independent priorities. One of
these is the relative importance of a particular application area when
compared to all other application areas; the other relates to the time
requirements of an individual application when compared to all others.
The automation committee should assign both of these priority ratings
to each project under consideration. The combination of the two ratings will determine the sequence in which the projects should be undertaken.

1. A letter priority (A, B, C, or D) should be assigned by the
committee to over-all functional areas, such as payroll, accounts re-

ceivable, and the like. Then, any individual project proposal falling into one of these areas will be assigned the letter priority of that area of application. Letter priorities are:

> A — Most important. All available resources are authorized if necessary.
> B — Essential. Rescheduling of some on-going projects may be authorized if necessary.
> C — Normal.
> D — Low. These are marginal projects whose implementation could be postponed with no deleterious effects on company operations.

The letter priority applying to any functional area may be altered by the automation committee from time to time to satisfy changing management objectives.

2. A number priority (1, 2, 3, or 4) should be assigned to each individual project under consideration. It is based on the following:

> — the urgency of the project,
> — the expected elapsed time to completion,
> — project development costs,
> — expected savings, and
> — expected increased profit.

> 1 — Most urgent. Expected completion date is already beyond the date on which completion is needed.
> 2 — Needed as soon as possible. This priority is based on the expected development costs and the expected operating savings or increased profit after installation. These projects can be expected to increase profitability substantially as soon as they are installed.
> 3 — Normal.
> 4 — Nice to have, but will have no significant impact on short-term savings or increased profit in relation to development costs.

Once a letter priority and a number priority have been assigned to each proposed project, the over-all priority of any project relative to all other projects can be recognized. Over-all priorities, from highest priority to lowest, are A1, B1, C1, D1, A2, B2, C2, . . . B4, C4, D4.

The priority system, and the clustering of priorities being assigned, should be examined from time to time by the automation committee. Frequent changes in priorities and the clustering of priority assignments around one or two ratings are both indications of trouble, and are easy to discover. In the former case, it is likely that, either not all relevant conditions were known to the automation committee at the time the original priority was assigned, such as the expected cost savings, or in the case of systems under development, significant slippages have occurred to warrant a rise in priority. If most systems pending and under development have the same urgent priority, the long-range data processing plan must be re-examined to bring the work the data processing department is expected to perform more in line with its capability.

An important factor in the success of the system is cooperation of users. All staff members, but particularly user management, should be thoroughly familiar with the priority classification system and the way in which priorities are assigned by the automation committee. Further, user management should be kept informed of the priorities of all pending and on-going system development projects. If a user wishes the priority of his system to be raised, he should be allowed to present his case to the automation committee (*not* to the data processing manager alone) along with any new data that may have a bearing on the situation. The representation of user management on the automation commitee should allow equitable and reasoned resolution to any conflicts. In addition, the data processing manager will not be solely responsible, since the assignments are made by the automation comittee as a whole.

A priority scheme is easy to develop, easy to understand, and easy to administer. It will be of great help to the data processing manager in project control by giving him a clear-cut designation of the manner in which he should apply his resources for the best possible return to the company.

9/ TIME ESTIMATING
AND PROJECT PLANNING*

When the project has been authorized and a priority assigned by the automation committee, it is the task of the data processing manager to make estimates and plan the project. It must be understood from the beginning that all planning is subject to revision, based on analysis of progress at each of the subsequent checkpoints. Refer again to Figure 1, the Project Control Cycle, in Chapter 6.

Project planning includes

— stating in detail the tasks to be performed,
— establishing individual project checkpoints,
— designating the skills required to perform each task,
— estimating the time to complete each task,
— assigning appropriate personnel to each task, and
— scheduling the tasks.

The last two functions, because of their complexity, will be covered in the next two chapters.

The Detailed Task Outline

During the project initiation process, a list of tasks is drawn up for the particular project under consideration, using as a guide the *Sample Task List* given in Exhibit 5. Modifications and further task breakdowns should be made as needed to suit individual needs. For example, the task "conduct interviews" might be divided into the sub-tasks of

*Dick H. Brandon, *Management Standards for Data Processing,* Princeton: D. Van Nostrand Company, Inc., 1963. A more complete discussion of performance standards is given in Chapters 8, 9, 10.

Exhibit 5: Sample Task List

General	Study Phase	Analysis Phase	Design Phase	Programming Phase	Implementation
Identify present problem.	Develop study plan.	Forms analysis.	Design reports.	Review of specifications.	Organize system test.
State objectives and anticipated benefits from new system.	Interview user management.	Reports analysis.	Design files.	Logic design and block diagramming.	Conduct system test.
	Collect existing documentation.	File analysis.	Design input documents.	Desk checking.	Review system test with user.
Define project scope.		Analyze information requirements.	Design clerical procedures.	Coding.	
General survey of user operations.	Collect operating statistics and cost data.	Procedure analysis.	Write programming specifications.	Program test data creation.	System and operating documentation.
Preliminary general design.	Collect sample documents.	Develop alternatives.	Test material collection.	Testing.	Monitor system performance.
Preliminary cost estimate.	Observe present process.	Cost analysis.	Management presentation.	Program documentation.	
Assign resources to project.	Summarize present system.	Management presentation.			
Develop project schedule.	Present study results to management.				
Develop project budget.					

constructing an interview guide stating the subjects to be covered in the interviews, holding the interview, and reviewing and preparing a summary of the interview.

By developing such detailed lists of tasks, a base is established for estimating, and the requirements for differeing skills are highlighted. This detailed task listing may also be used to specify the organizational component responsible for each sub-task. The *Project Management Responsibility Chart* shown in Exhibit 6 should be used for this purpose.

Project Checkpoints

Checkpoints are established at each transfer point in the project. For example, the transfer of a system design specification to the programming function is a checkpoint, as is the transfer of completed programs to the operations department. Other checkpoints include the completion of any task where a tangible output is produced, such as an element of documentation, a flow-chart, or a block diagram. The purpose of this kind of checkpoint is to verify that the work performed thus far has been completed satisfactorily and according to installation quality standards.

Another type of checkpoint is the contingency checkpoint. Certain tasks may be identified as critical to a project or may have had a history of difficulty in other projects. Such tasks may be highlighted by making a "trouble" forecast or contingency plan early in the project. For these, reviews may be held shortly after the beginning of the task and at periodic points throughout the performance of the task. Planning might also include prediction of problems that might be disclosed during review and possible corrective actions.

Designation of Required Skills

The skills and experience required to perform each task must be stated explicitly to provide a guide to personnel assignment. Typical skills required by tasks are discussed in the chapter on personnel assignment.

Estimating Task Completion Time

An estimate of task completion time is the prediction of the amount of time required to perform a given task. It follows that the activities

Exhibit 6: Project Management Responsibility Chart

Date_____

Project No._____ Project Name _____

PROJECT MANAGEMENT RESPONSIBILITY CHART

Task	Performance			Review		
	Primary	Partici pating	Consulting	Working	Managerial	Executive

constituting a task must be known before a meaningful estimate can be made. Several levels of estimates are therefore developed during a project. Preliminary estimates of systems development activities may become firm detailed estimates after the systems study phase is completed. Programming cannot be estimated closely until the programming specifications are known. Initial estimates of programming work can be refined at the conclusion of system design. It is generally the responsibility of the project leader to maintain the integrity of the estimating procedure by attributing precision in estimates only to those tasks which are close at hand. Some basic rules for estimating are:

- Know all possible details about a task prior to estimating the time it will require.
- Delay final estimates for a task until prerequisite tasks have been finished.
- Be conservative.

APPROACHES TO ESTIMATING

Any staff member who may be called upon to furnish estimates should be aware of the three approaches which may be taken — the intuitive, the historical, and the standardized.

Intuitive Approach

The *intuitive approach* requires reliance on an individual's ability to combine history, standards, and his personal experience in an informal way to arrive at the estimates. Some people are quite good at estimating in this fashion. They seem to arrive at a relatively accurate figure instinctively, and when such a person is available, this approach has advantages.

We cannot, however, rely upon having such persons on the staff, or on recognizing them if we do. Fortunately, *the historical approach* can be just as accurate. It involves comparing the present project tasks to those of a *similar* past project. Differences between the projects are noted and the actual time expended on the former project is adjusted and used as the estimate for the new project. This approach, however, requires truly *comparable* projects and good time records.

Standardized Approach

The *standardized approach* is best suited to tasks which can be clearly defined and which are performed frequently. Two types of standards are required:

- methods standards to define the tasks and associated work practices, which are assumed throughout this book, and
- performance standards defining the expected time to complete each portion of the work.

Because the nature of systems analysis tasks vary less from one project to another than do the programmer's, and because programming tasks are more easily segmented and defined, the historical approach is generally easier for systems analysis. Standardized estimating is more accurate for programming tasks.

The standards approach is not as commonly used nor as well understood as it should be. The remainder of this chapter, therefore, is devoted to a discussion of the standards technique of time estimating for system analysis, programming, and machine requirements.

The standards approach can be useful because it can be employed quickly and easily at an early stage of a project, yet yield usable estimates. To illustrate this approach, we will use computer programming as the function which is most easily understood and for which standards are most easily established and validated.

Estimating Standards

The basic steps in establishing estimating standards for a function such as programming are:

- Establish or define the method and tasks to be used.
- Standardize the methodology by which the tasks are to be performed.
- Determine the variables involved in the performance of the tasks.
- Establish time relationships between the various parameters and the tasks.
- Derive standards for each of the tasks.
- Use these standards in developing a schedule.
- Evaluate the data on actual performance.
- Modify the standards if necessary.

The basic tasks in the programming process can be defined for purposes of estimating to be:

1. Orientation and preliminary logic design
2. Detailed logic design
3. Coding
4. Test planning and test data preparation
5. Compilation and testing
6. Documentation and installation assistance

PROGRAMMING PARAMETERS

A far more difficult task is to determine the parameters by which programming time will vary for each of these tasks. The scope and types of parameters which affect the time and cost of programming fall into three different categories:

1. Environmental factors
2. Factors relating directly to the program
3. Loss factors

Environmental Factors

The environmental factors which affect the performance of a function generally are constant for a given data processing installation performing that function in the same environment each and every time. Environmental factors clearly include *the type of machine* for which the program is to be developed, *the language* in which the program is to be written, *the physical environment* in which the programmer works, and of course *the methodology* predefined for the programmer. All these factors have a significant effect on the cost of programming, but none of them varies from one computer program to the next. Thus, the extent to which documentation is required will of course affect significantly the documentation time; however, it will affect equally the documentation time for each and every type of program.

Program Parameters

The second category of variables are those which relate to the particular element of each of the different computer programs. In general, it is possible to summarize these into three specific categories — program size, program complexity, and program data base.

Program Size   *Program size* is essentially linear in its impact on programming time. This can be defined as the number of instructions, the number of lines of coding, or more simply, the number of pages of coding. In fact, within the range of accuracy that programming time and cost can be estimated, in general assumed to be no better than one-half day per task, it is entirely possible to estimate program size to within *ten pages of coding*. Thus it is simpler to define a unit of size as ten pages of coding, or perhaps 180 lines of coding, depending of course on the methodology standards developed relating to the number of lines of code per page.

Program Complexity   *Program Complexity* is somewhat more difficult to define and is much more subjective to estimate as well. The simplest technique for estimating program complexity, which embodies a number of factors, is to use the technique known in industry as the "SAD" rating. SAD is the acronym for Simple, Average, Difficult, and is essentially a division of the universe of tasks into three categories, in such a way that one-third of each of the tasks falls into each category. In analyzing program complexity, however, it appears that it is not possible to use only three categories, since the difference between a simple and an average program could be significantly more than one-half day of preparation time, thereby exceeding the range of accuracy within which we want to work. Thus, the simplest approach again is to expand the number of categories in which programs are placed, for purposes of defining complexity. Six categories are used and are considered sufficient to allow both reasonable estimating and reasonable accuracy in forecasting time:

    A. Simple
    B. Moderate
    C. Average
    D. Difficult
    E. Extremely difficult
    F. Impossible

The final category, F, does not refer to the impossibility of writing the program, but rather to the impossibility of using an essentially linear rating scheme to relate the time of performance to the complexity. A program rated F is so complex that the amount of time required to program it is so much greater than a program rated E that it cannot be estimated accurately to within one-half day. Exhibit 7 indicates the types

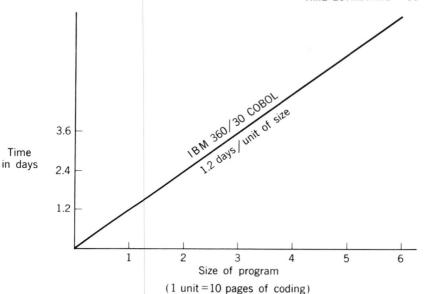

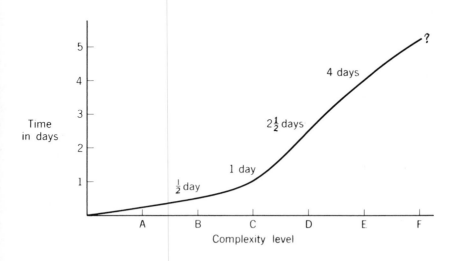

Exhibit 7: Time Relationships for Task 3–Coding

of time relationships which will be developed and indicates therefore why an "impossible" program becomes difficult to measure.

Program Data Base   *Program data base*, the third variable, generally relates to the number of files or data bases to be treated by the program. This could be defined as the number of formats of data base used, or it could be simply a count of the number of files or component elements of the hardware manipulated by the system. Alternatively, a weighted count could be given to each component of the hardware. For example, a disk might be given a rating of 3, a tape file a rating of 2, and the production of a printed report or the reading of a punch card, 1. The sum total count then is one measure of the complexity of data base manipulation. In large-scale data-base-oriented systems, it may be further possible to modify this count by the number of data base elements, or formats which modify the data base and which make the programming more difficult. Or this could be included as a factor in the complexity rating assigned to the program.

Once the program elements and parameters have been defined, it becomes possible to estimate time relationships, such as those illustrated in Exhibit 7, for each of the different variables.

Loss Factors

The third class of parameter, loss factors, are factors which should be taken into account if the estimates and the actual performance vary significantly because of outside factors that could not be taken into account at the time of estimating. Such outside factors would include inadequacy of systems design, changes made by the user during the programming process, inability to access machine time for testing on a convenient schedule, and a number of other factors. These factors should be delineated so that they can be isolated when they occur, so that the variance can be properly attributed. If a significant variance is continually ascribed to a specific set of loss factors, the cause of the loss factors must be corrected.

Establishing Time Relationships

Once the parameters have been completely defined, it becomes necessary to establish time relationships for each of these parameters for each task. Clearly these time relationships cannot be standardized across the entire data processing industry, since there are a number of environmental factors which differ from installation to installation and from one type of machine to another. These factors were outlined before; the most significant difference between them is probably the methodology under which the programming is to be performed, which is necessarily different from installation to installation. As a result, it can only be done at the installation level, where the methodology is properly defined and where unique time relationships can be developed.

However, it is possible to establish some general guidelines for the method by which these time relationships can be defined. For example, the first step takes the task as defined and breaks that task into its smallest component steps, effectively simulating the technique used in time and motion study. Thus Task 1, orientation and initial logic, can be broken into a number of sub-steps such as:

— reading the specification,
— evaluating the file layouts,
— segmenting the program into major logical components, and
— developing an over-all block diagram for each component.

Once the tasks are defined, it is possible to define for each sub-tasks exactly which parameters affect the cost involved. Thus, evaluation of the file layouts is a direct function of the variable previously identified as program data base. A program with three files will take one-half as long to evaluate as a program with six files.

Similarly, the segmentation of the program is directly correlated to the complexity of the program and the complexity of the system specification, which is again directly related to the program complexity.

At this point, it is possible to estimate the range of time needed for the performance of each sub-task. For example, the reading of a specification could take from one-half hour for the simplest of all specifications to possibly four days for a very complex E-level type computer program. This, then, would give some insight into the range of time needed for the varying levels of the parameters defined. By performing this type of analysis, it is possible to construct a table or simple list which will indicate that the time required to perform Task 1, for example, might be one-half day for each level of complexity, plus one-quarter day for each file. Similarly, comparable time relationships would have to be developed for each of the tasks and sub-tasks in the programming process. (Exhibit 8 gives an example of this.)

Exhibit 8: Construction of Time Relationships

Tasks	Size	Complexity	Data Base	Sample Ranges
Task 1 – Macro-Logic				
Read Specification		✓		½ hour – 30 hours
Review File Layouts			✓	½ hour/file
Segment Program		✓		1 hour – 20 hours
Block Diagram		✓		½ hour – 10 hours
Review with Analyst		✓		1 hour – 8 hours
Task 2 – Micro-Logic				
Segment Each Element	✓	✓		½ hour – 4 hours/element
Diagram – Level 2	✓	✓		1 hour – 8 hours/element
Review		✓		½ hour – 8 hours
Task 3 – Coding				
Code	✓	✓	✓	8 hours/150 lines
Review	✓			½ hour – 2 hours/150 lines
Add Linkages		✓		½ hours – 8 hours

Thus, Task 1 Summary:
A – ½ day
B – 1½ days
C – 4 days   } Plus ½ hour/file
D – 6½ days
E – 8 days

Systems Analysis

Similar techniques can be applied to the process of systems analysis, although accuracy in this area may be somewhat difficult to achieve. Where it is possible to develop time relationships for programming which allow estimating to within one-half day per task, it is generally not as simple to develop estimates for systems analysis. Thus, a range of two to three to five days per task might be acceptable for a function such as systems analysis, which on the whole will take far more time than the writing of a single program.

Again the variables involved in systems analysis are comparable. Environmental factors which include the machine and its component elements, the standards for systems analysis methodology, and the

physical environment are not significantly different from those used in programming. Factors describing the systems design, however, are considerably different. They include:
- breadth and complexity of the system itself,
- the number of programs into which the system is expected to be broken,
- the number of files,
- the number of documents to be examined,
- the number of functions to be interviewed,
- the number of organizational elements affected by the system, and a host of other possible parameters.

It should be noted that the complexity of systems analysis tasks does not necessarily have any relationship to the complexity of the corresponding programming tasks. Consider, for example, a system in which the programs are to be run in a variety of combinations in the multi-programming mode: It would be primarily the task of the systems analyst to specify, in advance, the characteristics of each program in such a way that the combinations would operate efficiently. This type of planning must be done by analysts and cannot be left to individual programmers, who may have no way of knowing the characteristics of other programs in the system, or of those in other systems, with which their own might be paired.

Estimating System Breadth and Complexity. Certain standard system functions characterize the operation of any business data processing system. These standard functions are:
1. Data collection
2. Data edit
3. Error correction
4. Data sequencing
5. Collating
6. Calculation
7. Data transfer
8. File access
9. File update
10. Inquiry response
11. Data summarizing
12. Report preparation
13. Printing
14. Report distribution

Preliminary estimates of the scope of each of these functions in the new system will provide an outline of its over-all complexity.

Estimating Complexity of Analyst Functions. Normal functions performed by a systems analyst can be classified as follows:

(1) Study Phase
   (a) Gather operating statistics and documentation
   (b) Conduct interviews
   (c) Observe processes
   (d) Collect file and report samples
   (e) Write description of present system

(2) Analysis Phase
   (a) Analyze each document and file
   (b) Correlate information usage
   (c) State functional requirements
   (d) Develop systems alternatives

(3) Design Phase
   (a) Design new files
   (b) Design new output
   (c) Design new input
   (d) Design new procedures
   (e) Design new program specifications

The complexity of the analysis function is based upon the description of the system arrived at in the first step. For example, if in the present system it is determined that there are 50 data collection points, it can be assumed that the analyst must gather operating statistics from all 50 stations and must include interviews for them in his project plan.

As the systems development process evolves, additional system characteristics will become apparent, which may alter the original estimate. Thus, control points must be established at which revision in estimates for later tasks may be developed.

The System Development Estimating Guide, show in detail in Chapter 15, is used to estimate all system development functions through final system design and documentation. The Guide assumes that each of the analyst functions will take a standard length of time. These times may be adjusted as experience dictates.

Summary

To briefly summarize the steps discussed thus far, the data processing manager has prepared a detailed task outline, established the project checkpoints, and made estimates for the first phases of the project. As work progresses, a review is held at each of the previously established checkpoints, and estimates for the next tasks refined. At the end of the system design phase, estimates of programming time will be adjusted to take into account more accurate assessments of the parameters involved.

OTHER FACTORS

Two other factors must be considered before final estimates are developed. They are
— the analyst's or programmer's experience, and
— slack time.
There are a number of ways of adjusting the estimates in the light of the experience of the individual. If the individual is known at the time the estimates are made, it is an easy matter to either adjust the estimate upward or downward (or leave it as is) to correspond to his expertise and previous performance relative to the estimates. If the individual is not known at the time the estimates are made, a note is added that the estimate is based on the assumption that an "average" programmer will be assigned. Variances can then be attributed to the individual as well. Alternatively, the manager might specify in advance that a certain level of programmer must be assigned to a particular program, and the estimates made accordingly. Personnel assignment is discussed more fully in the next chapter.

If *historical* statistics have been used to establish the estimating standards, a certain degree of slack time will already be built into them. In this context, "slack time" is taken to mean a cushion against unexpected delays. The fact that these delays do occur — and the variety of things that can go wrong to delay programming or analysis — does not need to be stressed here. Because it is better to err on the side of overestimating than underestimating, the estimator must keep in mind that some slack time should be included in the estimates, if it has not been taken into account in setting the standards in the first place.

Once the standards have been established for the installation, it will be possible to make increasingly accurate estimates of the time required. Consideration should be given to the possibility of automating the manipulation and reporting of these standard statistics, not only for programming but for other tasks in the system development process. (Appendix A describes some software packages for project control.)

Along with programming estimates, estimates of computer time are required. To estimate the computer time which will be required for development of a system, it is necessary to estimate separately the time which will be required for compilations or assemblies and that which will be required for program testing.

After a program has been rated for complexity and size, it is possible to establish the expected compiler time. The number of compilations needed is a direct function of size and complexity. Standards should be developed in the installation for each language, machine, and operating system combination in use, for both the number of compilations and the time for each program unit. Before these are available, experienced programmers may be used to obtain subjective estimates. The manufacturer's literature and timed tests may also be used. Thus, knowing the compilation time required for each unit of program size, one can determine the total time required for compiling each program.

The number of test shots required for a specific program is related to program size, complexity, and number of files handled by the program. Again, each installation should develop standards based on its particular environment, and experience.

After calculating the number of shots required by the program, it becomes necessary to determine the length of the average test shot. This can be determined empirically by analysis of installation data. Then the average test time is multiplied by the calculated number of test shots to arrive at the estimated test time for the program.

The estimated test time is added to the time estimated for compilation or assembly to arrive at the total estimated equipment utilization for a program. This same procedure must be applied to all programs in the system.

Recommended forms for documenting estimates are illustrated in Section 3.

However good the estimating is, it can never be absolutely accurate because of loss factors and unexpected developments, and simply because of the "human factor" in both the estimating *and* the work. That is why the checkpoint approach is necessary; it allows continual review and adjustment, and correction after review of *small* elements of the total task. Using this approach can make project control an extremely useful tool.

10/ PERSONNEL ASSIGNMENT

After the data processing manager has done the preliminary work of stating the tasks, establishing checkpoints, and making time estimates, he must assign personnel to the project team. The job really began with the designation of skills required for each phase of the project.

Typical skills required for the systems analysis function are:

- investigative skills, required in data gathering and in systems testing,
- writing skills, required in reporting progress, preparing documentation, and selling systems concepts to users,
- analytical skills, required in formulating system requirements, and
- creative skills, required in detailed systems design.

Some of the skills required for programming are:

- analytical skills, required for understanding systems specifications,
- creative skills, required in logic formulation activities, and
- investigative skills, required for "debugging."

In addition, for a particular project, certain experience may be required of the programmer—for example with certain hardware, languages, and operating systems, software packages used in-house, and their application.

Flexibility may be maintained in the utilization of personnel by picturing each task as requiring a configuration of specific skills rather than particular people. For example, user personnel may perform certain data gathering tasks and help diagnose systems test results; certain programmers who are adept at debugging might be used to help desk-check and debug all programs in addition to writing some of the programs.

These and other adjustments require that management of the research and development function have available a summary of skills of user and installation personnel. While this is normally accomplished informally, larger installations may wish to establish a formal skills inventory, updated during personnel review cycles.

A sample of such a skills matrix is shown in Exhibit 9. The characteristics shown in the exhibit are illustrative only. Each company should develop its own set of skills for the matrix to reflect equipment, software, applications, and characteristics by which staff members are rated. A separate matrix should be developed for each job function in the data processing department.

It is recommended that the matrices be devised so that each staff member may be rated on each skill simply with a "yes" or "no." The most straightforward method of entering the individual data on the form is with a check mark indicating "yes," the individual has this skill or capability. Otherwise, the column is left blank. This simplified format will allow staff selection for a particular project to be done fairly easily, as is shown below.

Skills matrix: programmers	Machines and languages					Applications Experience					Characteristics			
Name_____	IBM 1400	CDC 7600	COBOL	Autocoder	BAL	Payroll	Acc'ts rec.	Invent. control			Fast coding	Fast debug.	Good doc.	No supr. needed

Exhibit 9: Sample Skills Matrix

Exhibit 10 is a sample of the type of form that may be used for choosing project development team members. Identifying information is entered at the top; a list of skills and characteristics required is entered in the column headings. Again, a different set will probably be required for each of the different types of jobs to be filled. For example, previous experience with the same or a related application may be important for the systems analysts, but not for the programmers; knowledge of the programming language to be used may be critical for programmers but not for systems analysts, and so on.

The names of all people eligible for assignment are entered on the selection form. This may include only those individuals free for assignment; or, if the project has a high enough priority to warrant removing a person from another project, it might include *all* individuals in that job classification. Then, using the skills matrix, transfer the ratings from the matrix to the corresponding columns on the selection form. A simple 0 or 1 score may be used for yes or no. Or each factor may be assigned a weight on a scale from 1 to 10 according to its importance to the project. For example, it might be very important that

Project: Tasks: Name___		Appl. Exp.	Knows lang.	Knows machine	No supr. needed						Total points

Exhibit 10: Sample Staff Selection Matrix

programmers know the language to be used, so that would be assigned a weight of 10. A programmer who knows the language gets a score of ten; one who does not a score of 0, and so on. When the scores of all individuals for each required skill have been entered, the points for each individual are added. The highest score will indicate the first choice for assignment. If more than one person is needed, they can be selected in the order of their scores. Alternates can then be designated on the basis of the next highest scores.

A most critical skill, of course, is that of project management. The three most important variables are:

- supervisory experience and ability,
- research and development experience on the equipment to be used in the project, and
- knowledge of the application.

As these skills are less easily quantifiable as missing or present, selection of project leaders and team supervisors is a less objective process. Candidates for selection may, instead, be rated weak ("w") or strong ("s") on each of the critical factors. The resulting selection table might look like this:

				CANDIDATE:				
FACTOR	1	2	3	4	5	6	7	8
Supervisory experience	w	w	w	w	s	s	s	s
Equipment experience	w	w	s	s	w	w	s	s
Application knowledge	w	s	w	s	w	s	w	s

The only certain claim which can be made for this rather crude rating scheme is that candidate number 1 (weak in all areas) would be undesirable and that candidate number 8 (strong in all areas) is the best choice. Between these two extremes, management must determine which factors are most crucial for a project leader in a given project and, more important, what type of management support and additional training can be provided in a brief period. Where such support cannot be given, the project leader's deficiencies may become a factor in softening the schedule.

Selection of back-up personnel, as mentioned earlier, should be given careful consideration. As a minimum, the data processing manager should, at the time of initial project team selection, identify individuals who would be qualified to step in and work with the project team in an emergency, either because a previous team member has left the project, or because progress analysis at a checkpoint has revealed the danger of slippage which assignment of additional personnel can alleviate.

If there is no one in the department who could act as back-up, the manager should consider additional training for some staff members, so that they could be assigned to the project if necessary. If there are no personnel with the required skills, so that initial team members have to be trained, the prudent manager will include in the training group an extra individual (or more than one) as insurance.

On extremely critical projects, "understudies" can be assigned to key project members, While they will not actually perform any work on the project unless an emergency arises, they follow the team's progress and maintain acquaintance with the documentation as it is developed, so that, if necessary, they could pick up work on the project with a minimum of orientation.

The cost justification for this type of back-up is easy to work out; the cost of possible delay to the company is balanced against the cost of understudy time *and* the consequences of not having the understudy available for other work while he is reviewing the critical project material.

Summary

In summary, there are three major steps in personnel assignment,

— identification of required skills at each job level,
— preparation and maintenance of the skills matrix, and
— personnel selection for individual projects based on the skills matrices.

The first two tasks are not directly related to any particular project, and are carried out in advance by top-level data processing management, possibly in conjunction with the personnel department of the company. The final task of selection and assignment of individuals to a project team requires the use of the skills matrices and a list of skills critical to the project in question.

11/ SCHEDULING

Estimating, which determines how much manpower or how many man-days, are needed to complete the job, is done as a preliminary to scheduling. The goal of scheduling is to determine how much elapsed time will be taken to complete the job. Scheduling requires explicit statements of the assumptions made about availability of computer time for testing, the availability and proficiency of user personnel, training requirements, and the time which must be devoted to administrative and other non-technical functions. A timetable — the schedule — is then developed to indicate the target date for each project task.

A large proportion of the apparent over-runs of project completion dates could be eliminated by the use of proper scheduling techniques. Accurate scheduling is not just a matter of being able to estimate accurately the length of time a set of tasks will take; consideration must also be given to the availability of people and equipment, and, a factor most often overlooked, the implications of the sequence of events which must take place. As a simple example, consider the case of the programming manager who assigned his least experienced programmer to the easiest program in the system. Rather obvious, one might think, but the project suffered seriously because of two factors that the manager overlooked. The first was that the "easy" program was the key element in reaching the completion date; if that program was not finished on time, the entire project would grind to a halt until it was. The other factor was that the programmer had no slack time; the manager had estimated that the program would take one month to complete, and he assigned the programmer exactly one month before the completion date. As a result, for every day the program was late, every member of the project team sat around doing nothing. The solution, of course, is that it is necessary to identify such key elements of the development tasks and allow for them in the schedule. There are various techniques available for this.

There are four commonly recognized types of schedules:
— milestone charts,
— wall-charts
— Gantt charts, and
— networks.

The advantages and disadvantages of each are described below. The data processing manager should choose one or more of these types, of modifications of them, as best suits the environment and work load of the installation. He may wish to use the easier but less comprehensive methods for short-term or non-critical projects and the more complicated types for extensive projects.

Milestone Charts

The simplest and easiest types of schedules to prepare are milestone charts. For each team member, a page is prepared listing the tasks to be accomplished. The estimated time required is entered, and then the completion date for the task. Columns should be left for recording actual completion times and any comments. The disadvantage of this type of schedule is that if fails to provide for interaction with other scheduled jobs.

Wall Charts

Numerous types of *wall charts* may be purchased. No detailed description will be given here, as the formats vary considerably. Information about them may be obtained from the suppliers, who advertise regularly in data processing magazines. The advantages of wall-charts are that they are clear, legible, and may be changed easily; however, they are expensive compared to other techniques, and their value has not yet been proven.

Gantt Charts

A *Gantt chart* is a graphic illustration of milestones. An example is given in Exhibit 11. The dates are listed across the top; the tasks to be accomplished are listed down the left-hand side. Milestones of the percentage of each task to be completed by a certain date may be shown at the bottom. Space is left for entering the percentage of work actually completed by each date. "Steps" are drawn in to relate the task to the dates. These may be colored in or cross-hatched as they are completed, to show progress to date at a glance. Gantt charts are easy to read and to update, but can be complicated to install as a standard technique. In addition, they do not give a complete picture of the interrelationships between tasks.

Networks

Networks overcome the disadvantage of the other types of schedules, in that they show all task interactions. PERT (Program Evaluation and Review Technique) is particularly useful in illustrating the interdependence of events within the project. (It is possible here to give only a brief outline of the methods of PERT and its usefulness in scheduling. Appendix C contains a bibliography for additional reading.) A PERT network is a graphic description of a plan showing the sequential steps needed to reach a stated objective. The network must be comprehensive and include all the significant interdependencies and interactions required to reach the objective. Networks define activities, their sequence, and their interrelationships. An activity is shown in a network as an arrow.

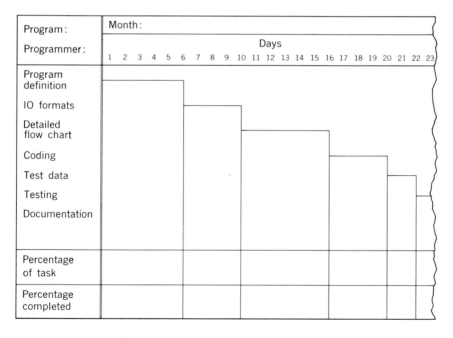

Exhibit 11: Sample Gantt Chart

Networks are an improvement over the Gantt chart, which shows activities but either does not indicate their relationships or, at best, indicates only a vague relationship in time. Networks are also an improvement over the milestone charts, which describe points in time when various items are complete or available but not the interrelationships among these items. These charts usually fail to identify the progress which must be made in one task before subsequent tasks can begin. PERT networks, unlike milestone charts, do recognize such prerequisites. The identification of activities and their points of interaction is an essential of networking.

By PERT definition, an event is a specific, definable accomplishment in a project plan, recognizable at a particular instant in time. Events do not consume time or resources. Activities, on the other hand, are the work efforts of a project. They represent the action of the network, such as interviewing, designing, programming, testing, etc. It is these time-consuming elements, whether they be human effort, use of facilities, or use of materials, that management must attempt to control. An activity is represented on a PERT network by an arrow which links two successive events, as shown in the example in Exhibit 12. While an activity is normally time-consuming, it may simply represent a relationship of interdependency between two events on the network. The result of such interdependency will be arrows with no activity name, indicating that a prior event must occur before subsequent activities can begin.

The time required to perform each activity in the network must be estimated. These estimates are based on

— planned manpower or other resources, and
— average resource application rates.

Because of the uncertainty involved in the duration of some activities, a range of estimates is usually made. In this case, an optimistic, a most likely, and a pessimistic time estimate is made for each activity. A statistically derived "expected elapsed time" for the activity is then determined from the three time estimates.

After calculating the expected times (t_e), these times are used throughout the various network paths to determine the total expected elapsed time for the project. This accumulated activity time establishes the expected completion date (T_E) for the project. T_E is also calculated for each event in the network.

Since there are several activities leading into some events, there

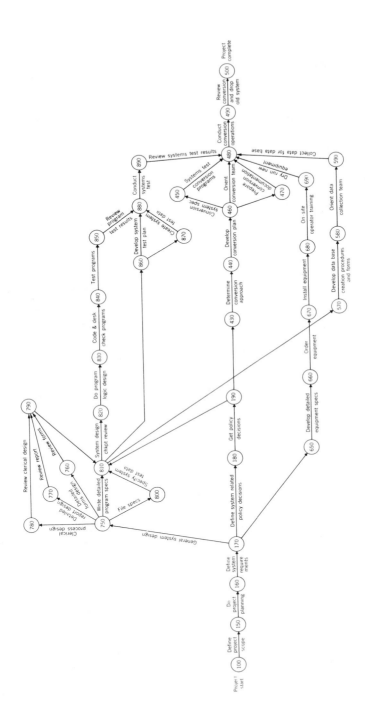

Exhibit 12: Sample Network for a System Development Project

will be a choice of T_E's for those events (one for each path leading into the event). Because an event cannot occur until all activities leading into it have been completed, the latest of these possible T_E's is assigned to the event.

T_L is defined as the latest calendar date in which an event can occur without creating delay in the expected completion date of the project. The T_L value for a given event is calculated by subtracting the sum of the expected elapsed times (t_e) for the activities on the longest path between the given event and the end event of the project from the latest date for completing the project.

Slack is the time difference between the latest allowable date and the expected date: Slack $= T_L - T_E$. It can have a positive, negative, or zero value. When the latest allowable date (T_L) is later than the expected date (T_E), positive slack exists. Positive slack is "time to spare."

The path in the network that has the minimum slack is the longest time path and therefore is called the critical path. It is characterized by the fact that a slip in an activity time along the critical path will cause an equal slip in the expected completion date of the end event. The critical path of a network will have slack equal to zero when $T_L = T_E$ for all events of that path through the network.

If the latest allowable date (T_L) for the end event occurs before the expected date (T_E) for the end event, the end event must be expected to occur behind schedule unless some action is taken. In this case, the critical path, and perhaps other paths, will have negative slack. Thus, management's attention is focused on the areas which most warrant remedial action.

It is possible to use PERT techniques as aids in resource allocation. Complete descriptions of resource allocation methods may be found in the literature of computer manufacturers offering resource allocation program packages. To use PERT techniques in resource allocation, it is necessary first to create a PERT network with estimates attached to each activity. Then one can schedule each task so that all resources are utilized as efficiently as possible and all tasks are completed as soon as possible. When appropriate resources are not available, task start times are adjusted to coincide with resource availability.

Summary

In summary, the *advantages* of networks over other types of schedules are that networks

—force attention to detail,

—enforce logical planning,

—reduce the risk of oversights, and

—are a good communications medium.

Their *disadvantages* are that they

—are time-consuming,

—are difficult to amend, and

—create problems in comparing actual to expected completion times.

TEST SCHEDULING AND CONTROL

The single most important, and most often neglected, area requiring scheduling expertise is that of *test control*. Test schedules are an integral part of the system development schedule and should be prepared by the individual responsible for the over-all development of the system. Test schedules serve three purposes:

—They provide the programmer and systems analyst with a timetable for their test processes.

—They serve as a guide for management in judging the progress of the project.

—They provide a basis for furnishing the operations personnel with necessary equipment and operator requirements.

Preliminary test schedules should include estimates of computer time requirements, and should be modified on the basis of actual computer use.

Checkpoints

When a test plan is prepared, checkpoints should be selected for verification of the progress of testing. Checkpoints can be established at specific time intervals or at project development milestones. The *Checklist for Test Planning,* Exhibit 13, will be found useful. Although testing of a program by someone other than the programmer is not necessary, it is highly desirable to give the test process more objectivity and create an opportunity to test the documentation.

Close attention must be given to the quality control. Determinations must be made of

—suitability of tests,

—thoroughness, and

—resource requirements.

Exhibit 13: Checklist for Test Planning

PROGRAM TESTING
A. Who is responsible for testing a particular program?
B. What data is needed for test?
C. Is input data to be simulated?
D. What resources are needed?
E. Does program to be tested use or feed other programs?
F. What output is expected?
G. Who is responsible for reviewing test results?

INTEGRATED PROGRAM TESTING
A. How many programs are involved?
B. Who is responsible for testing the package or group of programs?
C. What data is needed for test?
D. Who is responsible for reviewing test results?

SYSTEM TESTING
A. Where does data enter the system?
B. What data is needed for test?
C. Where will simulation/live testing be used?
D. Where will checkpoints be established?
E. What conversion method will be used?
F. Who is responsible for reviewing test results?

Standards should be established for

— types of data to be used,
— input/output restrictions,
— test submission (e.g., materials to be submitted for a test, procedures for routing of tests), and
— test analysis (e.g., debugging techniques, special diagnostic routines).

One of the important checkpoints in both programs and system testing is the completion of the test plan. A table of contents for a System Test Plan is given in Exhibit 14. Notice particularly that the areas of responsibility and test controls are detailed in the test plan and agreed to by the user and research and development before testing begins.

Program Test Plan

A Program Test Plan is given in Exhibit 15. Prepared before program testing is begun, it enables research and development management to determine that testing will be adequate and provides a guide for management on the progress of testing.

When errors are uncovered they should be corrected and the testing reinitiated to assure that changes and additions resulting from correction have not affected the previously tested modules. Revisions to the schedule should be made as frequently as necessary to reflect changes in the rate of progress during testing.

Reporting of progress is closely related to scheduling, as has been implied in this chapter. When creating the schedule, it is important to provide for recording of progress in a way that will facilitate comparisons with actual times, to allow accurate assessment of progress. Reporting and reviewing progress are discussed in the next two chapters.

Exhibit 14: Table of Contents – System Test Plan

1.0 General Information
    1.1 Cover Page
    1.2 Table of Contents
    1.3 Revision Page
    1.4 References
2.0 General Test Structure
    2.1 Test Objectives
    2.2 Areas of Responsibility
3.0 General Test Controls
    3.1 Input Controls
    3.2 Processing Controls
    3.3 Output Controls
4.0 General Test Procedures
    4.1 Submission of Tests
    4.2 Disposition of Test Results
    4.3 Documentation of Test Results
    4.4 Analysis of Test Results
5.0 Test Schedule
    5.1 Sequence of Tests
    5.2 Number and Frequency of Tests
6.0 Test Case 1*
    6.1 Resource Requirement
    6.2 Sample Transactions and Files
    6.3 Sample Expected Outputs and Files
    6.4 Test Procedure

*Follow this format for each test case (e.g., 7.0 Test Case 2, 8.0 Test Case 3).

Exhibit 15: Table of Contents – Program Test Plan

1.0 General Information
    1.1 Project Number
    1.2 Project Name
    1.3 Program Number
    1.4 Program Name
    1.5 Programmer
    1.6 Total Estimated Number of Test Shots
2.0 Test Case 1*
    2.1 Logical Test Number
    2.2 Purpose or Purposes
    2.3 Estimated Number of Test Shots
    2.4 Results of Each Test Shot

*Follow this format for each test case (e.g., 3.0 Test Case 2, 4.0 Test Case 3).

12/ PROGRESS REPORTING

The ability to evaluate project progress against a project plan is at the heart of project control. But progress evaluation depends on the collection and reporting of accurate and timely progress data.

The important factors of progress reporting are

— designation of checkpoints,
— progress recording, and
— trouble reports.

Progress Reporting Checkpoints

The checkpoints for progress should be defined in the planning stages of the project by the data processing manager in conjunction with the project manager. The recommended minimum set of checkpoints for progress reporting is shown in Exhibit 16. The number of checkpoints should be expanded for projects of substantial size and scope.

While conditions will vary from one installation to another and from one project to another, an effort must be made to ensure that checkpoint intervals are small enough for effective project control. One rule of thumb that can be given is that there should be a checkpoint at least once a month; every two or three weeks would be better for important projects.

Another rule of thumb is that a checkpoint should occur approximately every 15 man-weeks; as a result, projects with five men assigned will be checked every three weeks, larger ones with more than five men, at least once a week. The segmentation of checkpoints may be adjusted at various phases of the project according to the number of personnel assigned to each phase. If a project starts to slip badly, additional, more frequent checkpoints should be added to the schedule.

When the schedule is revised, dates for progress reports should be specified. Each project team member must be made aware of the existence of the checkpoints, and clearly understand what is expected of him at each one.

Recording Progress

The usual chain of reporting is upward from the individual team members (e.g., programmers and systems analysts) to the project manager to the systems or data processing manager. Project reporting may become the "weak link" in the project control cycle if the reporting responsibilities of each member of the team are not made clear and enforced.

Exhibit 16: Progress Reporting Checkpoints

1. System Study Completion
2. System Analysis Completion
3. System Design Completion
4. Coding Completion
5. First Stage of Program Testing
6. Final Stage of Program Testing
7. System Test Plan Completion
8. System Test — Intermediate Review
9. System Test Completion
10. Pre-conversion Preparation Completion

Emphasis should be placed on the necessity for *accurate* reporting. We wish to avoid the situation in which a program is reported as "90% complete" — week after week after week. A method for accomplishing this is to require each individual to estimate the time remaining to complete each of the tasks to which he is assigned. Such estimates have been found to be more reliable than estimates of percent complete. If desired, percent complete can be computed by

$$\frac{\text{Time to date}}{\text{Time to date} + \text{Estimated time to complete}}$$

Three types of documents are recommended for progress recording:

—the Checkpoint Schedule,
—the Individual Hours Recap, and
—a formal Progress Report.

Checkpoint Schedule   The checkpoint schedule, already mentioned, should be updated at each checkpoint, based on the Progress Report. The over-all schedule should, of course, be adjusted at each checkpoint as well, to reflect the findings of the Progress Report. As the expected task completion times are revised, the corresponding checkpoint dates must be brought up-to-date also. This task should be performed by the data processing manager or by the project manager; if the latter, it should be reviewed by the data processing manager.

Individual Hours Recap   The Individual Hours Recap, illustrated in Chapter 6, shows actual time spent, by task, by the individual project team members. This document may well be a time-sheet currently in use, with modifications if necessary. Time reporting may be on a weekly, bi-weekly, semi-monthly, or monthly basis. Under no circumstances should it be less frequent than one month.

Using the Individual Hours Recap, the project manager prepares his Progress Report, also illustrated in Chapter 16. A Progress Report should be prepared at each checkpoint. It shows activities, original man-day and dollar estimates, cumulative figures, and projections to completion. It may also be accompanied by a narrative report detailing any problems which have arisen in the reporting period and the results of past problem situations previously reported. The project manager should also specify what actions are being taken to overcome reported problems.

To summarize the planned recording process, Individual Hours Recaps are prepared by the team members at regular intervals; these are used by the project manager to prepare the Progress Report, which is reviewed by the data processing manager; the project schedule and corresponding checkpoint schedule are then adjusted to reflect progress to date. The technique of progress analysis is discussed in the next chapter.

Trouble Reports

One of the goals of the project control system is to spot potential trouble areas before they reach crisis proportions. Frequent checkpoints and intelligent analysis of progress reports are the key to this, but in addition a somewhat informal procedure for reporting problems should be encouraged. Every member of the project team should be made aware of his responsibility to complete the specific tasks assigned to him, but in addition, every team member should have responsibility for the *over-all success of the project*. If this attitude is properly fostered, each team member should take it upon himself to inform management of any possible problems he thinks may arise. If, for example, a programmer encounters difficulty in preparing a block diagram within the time originally estimated for that task, he should inform the project manager that the coding of the program may also take longer than planned. Conversely, he might decide that by deliberately taking longer on logical analysis, he can reduce coding time. The project manager should take this type of comment into consideration when making schedule adjustments.

Good reporting of progress, however, is not the only important factor. The manager must be able to analyze the reports and take appropriate corrective action to complete the control cycle. These considerations are discussed in the next chapter.

13/ REVIEW AND PROGRESS ANALYSIS

As part of the project planning task, the project manager and the data processing manager should determine not only what checkpoints are to be used in the project, but also what will be reviewed at each, and by whom. It should be kept in mind at all times that the goal is to spot problem areas *before* they reach emergency proportions, in time to take corrective action.

Progress Review

Exhibit 17, Review and Control Guide for Selected Checkpoints, lists some of the review checkpoints, responsibilities, and suggestions for analyzing the situation at each.

As an example of the use of the checkpoint list, consider the checkpoint at "Completion of Study." The list shows that user management as well as data processing management should participate in the review. The methods of review should be considered carefully. For example, one of the methods for review at the completion of the study, as given in the list, is to read the study report in detail. This is obvious enough, yet it frequently fails to get done. If a review at this point is to have any meaning, the report must be read, understood, and questioned by the departments responsible for the review.

The review guide also lists the items to which special attention should be paid. For example, on completion of study, one of these special matters is "user agreement on present system summary." These items will cause great difficulty and added expense later if not reviewed properly.

The problem listed as most likely to occur is, in fact, *extremely likely* to occur. Insufficient or inexact detail is a very common problem at this state of system development, and it is the responsibility of user

Exhibit 17: Review and Control Guide for Selected Checkpoints

Checkpoint	Reviewed by	How	What to Review	Most Likely Problem	Most Likely Correction
Project plan	D.P. mgmt. User mgmt.	Read and interview project leaders.	Task list for completeness. Mgmt. resp. chart. User/D.P. acceptance. Inclusion of review and control tasks.	Missing tasks.	Redo plan.
Completion of estimates	D.P. mgmt. User mgmt.	Read and interview. Consult standards. Consult benchmark projects.	Supporting detail. Conformance to plan.	Over-optimistic estimates.	Revise estimates Set re-estimate time.
Completion of schedule and budgets	D.P. mgmt. User mgmt. Exec.	Read and interview.	Resource assumption. Critical tasks. Cost factors used.	No recognition of lost time factors.	Establish more frequent review points.
First phase of systems study	Project manager	Interview.	Scope expansion. Is user fulfilling his commitment?	Unavailability of key user interviewees.	Meet with user.
Completion of study	User mgmt. D.P. mgmt.	Read in detail. Discuss. Interview the study team. Interview the user.	Exceptions discovered. Preliminary observations of users. User agreement on present system summary. Scope expansion.	Fuzzy details. Incomplete detail on exceptions.	Order more study and/or supplement study team.

Milestone	Who	How	What	Problem	Action
Completion of system analysis	D.P. mgmt. User mgmt.	Discussion.	Alternatives. True requirements. Design time estimates.	Reject non-machine solution.	Get cost estimates on alternatives.
Data base design completion	D.P. mgmt. User mgmt.	Read. Discuss with user. Interrogate project team.	User review file. Match new data base to all old files	Incomplete.	Evaluate extra item needed and redo design.
Systems design	D.P. mgmt. User mgmt. Exec.	Read. Intensive interview with project team.	Comprehensiveness. Exceptions handling. Controls. Error correction procedure. Programming estimates.	Incomplete coverage of requirements.	Determine if neglect items must be included in this project.
Coding completion	Project manager	Interview programmer. Look at program.	Standards. Language usage. Faithfulness to logic design.	Logic errors.	Rewrite.
Testing	Lead programmer Project manager	View test results.	Results vs. specs. Progress vs. test plan.	Not all of test plan executed.	More testing.
System test completion	User mgmt. D.P. mgmt.	View test results.	Test results vs. system test plan. Test results vs. specs.	Omissions.	Re-test or defer some features.
Conversion	User mgmt. D.P. mgmt.	Discussion	Conversion plan. Conversion staffing.	Inadequate staff.	Extend or simplify conversion effort.

and data processing management to prevent the project from proceeding before the deficiency is rectified. A suggested method of correction is also given in the guide.

Project Progress Analysis

The Progress Report produced at each checkpoint is the important document in the analysis of project progress. The report contains estimates of the percent complete for each phase of the system under development. These percent complete figures should be compared to the schedule to determine which phases, or units within a phase (such as individual programs), are on, ahead of, or behind schedule. Each behind-schedule condition must be analyzed to determine whether the slippage was due to a one-time difficulty or to a problem which can be expected to recur. On the basis of these analyses management can determine what corrective action should be taken.

Revision

After each Progress Report has been analyzed for corrective action, all schedules and budgets must be revised on the basis of progress to date. Before schedules can be revised, new estimates must be made for the work remaining in the phases or programs underway. The new estimate for work remaining should take into account only the figures for the work completed so far. The original estimate should be ignored.

For example, a particular program was estimated to require eighty man-days for logic, coding, and testing. Aften ten man-days of effort, the programmer reports it is 10% completed. Assuming that the remaining 90% of the work will proceed at the same rate as the 10% already completed, the most reliable estimate for the remaining work must be ninety man-days.

The methods used to create the original schedules and budgets should be used to generate the new ones. Automated project control systems such as PERT and resource allocation systems allow for such revisions to schedules. Under a revision, PERT systems will compute new slack values for activities, and will determine the new critical path resulting from schedule changes. Resource allocation systems will recompute the deployment of resources to reflect the changed conditions.

At the time of creating the new schedules and budgets, it would be unduly optimistic to assume that any particular anticipated corrective action will have any desirable effect on the *rate* of progress on the work underway. *New estimates and budgets should be based solely on the rate of accomplishment to date.* If corrective action turns out to indeed have positive effects, they will be reflected in the next Progress Report and will find their way into schedules and budgets developed at that time.

14/ COST ALLOCATION

The allocation of costs and comparison to budgeted expenditures is a function of data processing management and the automation committee. This area of project control, more than any other, will probably be dictated by previously established company policy and procedures. The documents produced, for example, will in an overwhelming majority of cases be pre-defined, so that data processing management has little choice in the format of cost reporting. For this reason, no documents for detailed cost allocation are specifically recommended in this book.

There are, however, a number of considerations in the allocation of system development costs of which the data processing manager should be aware, since cost control is one of the aspects of project control.

The costs of developing a system should be recorded and analyzed according to the type of resource used. Three types of resources are used in system development:

1. Manpower measured in units such as man-months.
2. Computer usage, measured in units of time such as hours of use for the central processing unit (CPU) of a computer.
3. Indirect costs, such as expenditure for supplies, expressed in dollars.

In addition, the costs of purchase and installation of new equipment may sometimes be attributed to a single project. Other indirect costs which must be considered as each occurs are one-time costs of personnel training, and the costs of purchasing and installation of data processing equipment other than computers, or of procedures, such as a project control system.

Manpower costs should be computed on the basis of the total cost per employee. Costs directly attributable to an employee include his salary and direct benefits paid by the employer, such as insurance, social security tax, and vacations. Other costs, of the general overhead variety, should not be included as a direct cost of manpower but as an indirect cost, along with supplies, etc. The hourly cost per employee should be used for all time spent by the employee, regardless of the type of work he is doing on the project at any particular time.

There are two methods of assigning the cost of computer time. One is the actual cost method; the total costs of the data processing operations department are accumulated for a period and divided by the number of machine hours to arrive at an average hourly cost, which, multiplied by the hours used per project, will give total computer time cost. The disadvantage of this method is that the charges to a particular project might fluctuate from month to month even though the total hours used by a project remained constant.

The second approach, standard costs, was developed to eliminate this disadvantage. A determination is made of realistically attainable number of productive hours. A standard hourly rate for the computer is derived by dividing the estimated total costs for the data processing department by the standard number of productive hours. The standard rate can then be charged to projects by multiplying the number of hours used by each project by the standard rate. If the actual hours and actual costs are the same as the standard, all costs of the data processing department will thus be allocated. If variances are continuing and substantial, it means that the standards need revision.

The advantage of standard costs is that the charges to each project will fluctuate in direct proportion to computer time used. This facilitates budgeting and yields more meaningful after-the-fact analyses of budgeted against actual costs.

When evaluating the Progress Report, comparison should be made between expenditures and budget to determine whether the percent completion of the project is according to budget, in the same manner as time comparisons are made.

There are, of course, a wide variety of uses to which cost allocation figures can be put in answering questions about how the system development process can be made more economical for the company. Some of these questions are listed below.

1. Is it better to hire inexperienced personnel and train them ourselves, or pay higher salaries to avoid training costs?
2. Would it be more economical to hire a consulting firm (on a contract basis) for certain projects or phases?

3. Would the company save money by renting outside computer time rather than upgrading or adding to present equipment?
4. Would it pay to invest in additional software to reduce debugging and/or programming time? (This assumes that the cost of the software is known.)
5. Would it be more economical, when additional man-time is needed, to hire more staff or to pay present staff to work overtime?

The discussion of cost allocation in this chapter has been devoted almost entirely to the system development process. The same remarks, however, can be made about the allocation of production costs. As it is an extremely complex subject, the interested reader is urged to pursue the subject with one of the large number of books on general cost accounting which are currently in print.

SECTION 3

DOCUMENTATION

INTRODUCTION

Data processing documentation is defined as a written record, organized into a series of descriptive documents, relating to all aspects of the system development process. It is necessary here to make a clear distinction between *development documentation* and *control documentation*. Gray and London, in their book, *Documentation Standards,** give these definitions:

> Development documentation is descriptive of a system itself, i.e., a system's operating performance characteristics, tools and materials. Development documentation is therefore the means of communicating information *about* the system.

> Control documentation on the other hand is concerned with communicating information about resources used to develop the system; it is therefore primarily concerned with project development organization, with personnel, time, materials and money.

There is, however, a certain amount of overlap between the types, for two reasons. The first is that standardized development documentation is a prerequisite for standard project control techniques, as was discuss in Chapter 3. Secondly, the monitoring of progress and quality is partially accomplished through review and analysis of the development documentation produced throughout the system development process. Because of the close relationship between the two types, it is difficult to discuss one without mentioning the other. It is for that reason that some of the more important development documents have been discussed, and examples given, at various points in this book.

This section is mainly concerned with those documents used in project control alone, i.e., those documents which may not already be in use in an installation that has heretofore not been using any form of project control.

*Brandon/Systems Press, 1969, p. 9.

The section is presented in three parts:

1. Chapter 15, which discusses documents needed for the initiation and estimating phases of the project, such as the Resource Requirements Forecast and the System Development Estimate Guide.
2. Chapter 16, giving examples of recommended progress documentation.
3. Chapter 17, which covers operating documentation such as operator and equipment logs.

All the documents discussed in this section have been referred to at various appropriate places throughout the book.

15/ INITIATION AND ESTIMATING DOCUMENTATION

A systems development project which is preceded by careful and well-documented planning by the automation committee, the data processing manager, the project manager, and user management has a far greater chance of success than one in which these essential first steps are skimped or passed over completely. The essential planning documents are

- User Request,
- Resource Requirements Forecast,
- System Development Estimate Guide,
- Program Development Estimate Completion Form,
- Estimate Summary, and
- Project Task Plan and Schedule.

While the exact titles and formats of these documents may vary from one company to another, the essence of each should be incorporated into any project control system.

The User Request

The User Request was discussed at length in Chapter 7. A recommended format is shown in Exhibit 18. The initiator fills in the title (identification) of the proposed project or system, his name and title, and the date on which the request is made. He then describes the problem; names the operating areas (departments or divisions) of the company that would be affected, any automated systems that may be involved (particularly if the request is for a change to a present system, for an upgrading of a present system, or a combination of a currently operational system with another or with current clerical procedures); and lists any documents that might have a bearing on the problem. If

Exhibit 18: User Request

Identification of Proposed Project _____ Date _____

_____

Requested by (name and title) _____

_____

Briefly state the problem to be solved: _____

_____

_____

What departments/divisions of the company will be affected? _____

_____

If known, what previously automated systems will be affected? _____

_____

What are the anticipated benefits (dollar savings, improved service)? _____

_____

_____

_____

What documentation is available for further study? _____

_____

If pertinent, by what date is the system needed and why? _____

_____

_____

Attach any additional data relevant to the problem. _____

_____

Authorized by: _____ Date: _____

Priority assigned: _____

If not authorized, state why: _____

_____

_____

there is a need for the system by a certain date (for example, to support expansion of a department or change in company procedure), he gives the date and an explanation. The initiator should attach to the form any other relevant data. Space is left for notations of committee action.

If the project is authorized, the next key document to be produced will be the System Proposal. The document and its place in the system development process were discussed in Chapter 4. As a review, the System Proposal is a preliminary description of a proposed approach to the project, prepared by the analyst. It contains, in addition to the design approach, a brief analysis of the present environment and a plan and schedule for implementation, including

— a statement of the objectives to be achieved,
— a statement of the process(es) that will be replaced, if any,
— a brief statement of the functions to be performed,
— the anticipated source of input data,
— the output desired, and
— use and distribution of data.

The Resource Requirements Forecast

In order to make authorizations and set project starting dates, the automation committee will need the Resource Requirements Forecast, Exhibit 19. The use of this form and the responsibility of management in preparing it were discussed in Chapter 7. The man and machine requirements are broken down into two six-month periods and beyond. Manpower requirements are broken down by type of work performed—analyst, programmer, machine operator, keypunch or encoding operator. Machine requirements are broken down by type of machine. This can be modified to provide for different types of equipment.

The Forecast contains information about all systems currently running on a production basis, and all authorized and on-going system development projects. It is not necessary to itemize production requirements. These can be shown simply as totals for all such jobs, because they are fairly inflexible. The figures for authorized and on-going system development projects must be shown individually to provide the information required for determining project selection and priorities.

The System Development Estimate Guide

This document, shown in Exhibit 20, was mentioned in Chapter 9 as the guide to estimating all tasks in the system study, system analysis, and system design phases.

Exhibit 19: Resource Requirements Forecast

Date _____

☐ Systems and Programming Personnel
☐ Computer Operations Personnel
☐ Equipment

Resource	Available (no. of days per month)	Project Number	Project Name	Requirements Current 6 mos.	Requirements Next 6 mos.	Requirements Beyond 12 mos.

The Guide is divided into five sections:

A. Interviews
B. Document Analysis
C. Conclusions and Recommended Approach
D. Presentation and Preparation
E. Final Design and Documentation

In each section, a certain number of man-days are allowed for each of the functions. For example, 0.5 man-days is allowed for each management interview, 1.0 man-days for each supervisory interview, and so forth. In Section B, 0.5 man-days is allowed for each input to be analyzed, 0.5 man-days for each report. Sections C and D are similar, where the man-days estimates for preparing design alternatives and presenting them to management are a function of the anticipated number of each of the items listed. Section E, Final Design and Documenation, depends for its values on the total man-day estimates developed in sections A, B, and C. A total man-day estimate can thus be computed for all system development functions through system design.

Following is a detailed description of the steps in completing the form.

Section A   In the column headed "Number," on line 1, insert the anticipated number of interviews to be held with management personnel. In the same column, on line 2, insert the anticipated number of interviews to be held with supervisory personnel. On lines 3 and 4, insert the anticipated number of interviews with technical and clerical personnel, respectively. Then, multiply each inserted number by the number next to it in the column headed "Factor," and write the result in the column headed "Base Days." (For example, if four management interviews were anticipated, four would be multiplied by the factor 0.5, and the result, 2.0, would be written in the column "Base Days" on line 1.) Then, multiply each number in the column headed "Base Days" by the number text to it in the column headed "Referral Allowance," and write the result in the column headed "Total." (Continuing with the example, if 2 appears in "Base Days" on line 1, it would be multiplied by the referral allowance of 1.20, giving a result of 2.4, which would be written on line 1 in the column headed "Total.") Add the values on lines 1, 2, 3, and 4 of the column "Subtotal," multiply the sum by 1.25, and write the product on line 6 of section A, and on line 1 of section E, in the column headed "Total."

Exhibit 20: System Development Estimate Guide

Project No._____ Project Name_____ Date_____

Estimated by_____

A. INTERVIEWS

Type	Number	Factor	Base Days	Referral Allowance	Sub-Total	Interrupt	Total
1. Management		0.5		x 1.20			
2. Supervisory		1.0		x 1.20			
3. Technical		1.5		x 1.50			
4. Clerical		0.5		x 1.50			
5. Total Man-Days – Interviews							

B. DOCUMENT ANALYSIS

Item	Number	Factor	Total
1. Input Form		x 0.5	
2. Report		x 0.5	
3. File Layout		x 2.0	
4. Machine Readable Input/Output		x 0.5	
5. Total Man-Days – Document Analysis		x 1.5	

C. CONCLUSIONS AND RECOMMENDED APPROACH

Item	Number	Factor	Total
1. Interviews		x 0.5	
2. Documents		x 0.5	
3. Functions in New System		x 1.0	
4. Variations Provided		x 1.5	
5. Subtotal			
6. Alternatives Presented			
7. Man-Days to Formulate Conclusions		x 0.25	

Exhibit 20: Continued

D. PRESENTATION AND PREPARATION

Item	Number	Factor	Total
1. Attendees		x 0.25	
2. Locations		x 0.50	
3. Approvals Required		x 1.0	
4. Charts Needed		x 1.0	
5. Man-Days – Presentation			

E. FINAL DESIGN AND DOCUMENTATION

Man-Days	Number	Factor	Total
1. Interviews (A5)		x 0.25	
2. Document Analysis (B5)		x 0.50	
3. Formulate Conclusions (C7)		x 0.50	
4. Total Final Design Man-Days			

Section B In the column headed "Number," on line 1, insert the anticipated number of input forms that must be analyzed. On line 2 of the same column, insert the anticipated number of reports that must be analyzed. Similarly, on lines 3 and 4 insert the number of files, documents, and card input/output forms to be analyzed. Multiply each inserted number by the number next to it in the column headed "Factor," and write the result in the column headed "Total." (For example, if it is anticipated that twenty reports will have to be analyzed, 20 would be multiplied by 0.5 and the result, 10, would be written on line 2 in the column headed "Total.") Then add the numbers in the "Total" column and write the result on line 5 of section B and on line 2 of Section E, in the column headed "Total."

Section C In the column headed "Number," insert the anticipated number of interviews, documents, old functions in system, new functions in system, and variations provided, on lines 1, 2, 3, 4, and 5, respectively. Add the numbers in the column headed "Number" and write the sum on line 6 in the same column. Multiply the number on line 6 by 0.25, and then multiply the result by the number of alternatives to be presented, and write the result in the column headed "Total" on line 7. Multiply each of the numbers in the column "Number" on lines 1, 2, 3, 4, and 5 by the number next to it in the column headed "Factor," and write the result in the column headed "Total." Add all the numbers in the column headed "Total" and write the sum on line 8, section C and on line 3, section E, in the column headed "Total."

Section D This section computes the number of man-days needed for presentation to management of the proposed system or systems. Insert in the column headed "Number" the anticipated number of attendees, the number of locations at which the presentation is to be given, the number of approvals which must be obtained, and the number of charts needed for the presentation. Multiply each entry by the number next to it in the column headed "Factor" and write the result in the column headed "Total." Add the numbers in the column headed "Total" and write the sum on line 5, section D. This is the number of man-days required for presentations.

Section E Multiply each number entered in section E by the number next to it in the column headed "Factor" and write the result in the column headed "Total." Add the results of the multiplications and write the sum on line 4, section E.

To find the total number of man-days to be allowed for all system development functions through final system design and documentation, add the results found on line 6, section A; line 5, section B; line 8, section C; line 5, section D; and line 4, section E.

Program Development Estimate Completion Form

The discussion on estimating programming time in Chapter 9 gave an outline of the methods of rating program complexity and program size, of developing time standards for the estimating task, and of applying the standards to size and complexity to arrive at the estimate for an individual program. Exhibit 21, the Program Development Estimate Completion Form, illustrates the format to be used in documenting the estimates.

The project number and name, the estimator's name, and the date are entered at the top. Program numbers and names are entered in the first two columns. The estimator then rates each program (or, if previously developed, enters the ratings) for complexity and size. Using the standards, he enters the expected number of man-days for each of the programming tasks. The six tasks into which programming is usually subdivided are:

1. Macro-logic analysis (which results in a macro-block diagram)
2. Micro-logic analysis (which results in a micro-block diagram and/or decision tables)
3. Coding
4. Desk-checking
5. Compiling and testing
6. Documentation

The man-days for the tasks are then added to arrive at the estimate for each program.

The Estimate Summary

The Estimate Summary, Exhibit 22, is used after programming estimates have been made. This form provides for detail listing of the estimates that have been developed for system analysis and design, and for programming and conversion. It should be part of the perman-

Exhibit 21: Program Development Estimate Completion Form

Project No._____Project Name_____Estimated by_____Date_____

Program No.	Program Name	Rating	1	2	3	4	5	6	Total

Exhibit 22: The Estimate Summary

Project No. _____ Project Name _____ Prepared by _____ Date _____

Development Effort Project Phase:	Development Man-Hours			Equipment Use		Contractor Dollars	Investment Dollars	Completion Date
	Analysis	Programming	Other	Type	Hours			
A. Systems Analysis and Design								
B. Programming and Conversion								
C. Installation								

Systems Operation (Annual)

Type of Expenditure	Estimate	
A. Equipment Use		
Type _____	_____	(hours)
Type _____		
Type _____		
Type _____		
B. Data Control	_____	(man-days)
	_____	(machine-hours)
C. Systems and Program Maintenance	_____	(man-days)
	_____	(machine-hours)
D. Estimated Annual Growth Factor	_____	(percent)

ent file for the system. During the course of the project, as new estimates are produced, they should be recorded on an Estimate Summary and filed.

The Project Task Plan and Schedule

The last project control document to be prepared in the planning phase is the Task Plan and Schedule. It is a summary of the estimating, assigning, and scheduling previously completed. A sample of the document is shown in Exhibit 23.

Part 1 contains the standard project identification data.

Part 2 summarizes the resources needed. These are divided into three sections.

—feasibility and analysis (systems analysts),

— programmers, and

— equipment.

Total estimated time is entered, with space left for actual times after the work has been completed.

Part 3 summarizes the individual tasks to be accomplished, divided between analysts and programmers. Number of man-days, scheduled start and end times, and the responsibility is entered for each task. Again, the "Actual" figures are entered when the work is completed.

The Project Task Plan and Schedule should become part of the permanent management file for the project. As estimates are revised, new Plan and Schedule forms should be prepared; however, previous ones should not be discarded, but left in the file.

The set of documents just described, if prepared properly, will give an excellent history of the project. The complete file for each finished project should be reviewed by management and by the automation committee to determine what lessons have been learned. Is estimating weak in a particular area? If so, what can be done about it? Where did the most serious slippage occur, and why? And so on. This learning phase is particularly important for data processing management and project management. A project control system is of no use if it does not serve as a learning tool; the summary documents are the key to the process.

Exhibit 23: Project Task Plan and Schedule

Part 1 – Project Identification

Project No.:	Project Name:	Prepared by:	Date:
Priority:	Completion Date:		

Part 2 – Resource Summary for Development

F/A		PROG.		EQUIPMENT	
Estimate	Actual	Estimate	Actual	Estimate	Actual

Part 3 – Tasks and Schedule

TASK DESC.	TYPE		MAN-DAYS TO COMPLETE	START		COMPLETE		RESPONSIBILITY
	F/A	P		SCHED.	ACT.	SCHED.	ACT.	

In addition to providing feedback to management, these documents can be used to evaluate the control system itself. Are any of the documents inadequate for the installation? Can one or more be modified or eliminated? Were enough checkpoints used? And so on. Further, they will provide a measure of progress in the application of control techniques. The benefits of a project control system can be most clearly seen in comparison with past projects. Percentages of over-runs, slippage, and the like of pre-control system projects (provided adequate figures are available) can be compared with post-control system figures to evaluate the effectiveness of the system. Further, the degree of improvement as all members of the data processing department become familiar with the techniques of project control can be measured in the same way.

Finally, in this context it must be stressed again that a project control system cannot be rigid; management must be willing and eager to modify procedures and documents to approach more and more closely the best possible system for the installation needs and environment.

16/ PROGRESS DOCUMENTATION

The techniques of progress reporting and evaluation were discussed in Chapters 12 and 13, respectively. The key to these techniques were the two documents which were mentioned,

— the Individual Hours Recap, and
— the Progress Report.

Individual Hours Recap

One of the most important documents in a project control system is a record of actual time spent on the project. It provides part of the source information needed for comparing actual progress against estimates. The Individual Hours Recap, Exhibit 24, should be used for this purpose. The Recap permits individuals to indicate how many hours were spent on different parts of the project in each of several weeks. The Recap can be used in conjunction with a time card or in place of a time card. The breakdown of project phases or units on the Recap should be the same as the breakdown used on the Progress Report.

Every staff member should be required to keep track of the time spent on each project and each task on a *daily* basis. The habit of jotting down, either on a desk calendar or on the Hours Recap itself, how one's time was spent each day is an easy habit to develop. The figures obtained will be much more accurate than if the individual tries to remember at the end of the reporting period exactly what he was doing, and for how long, several weeks or even a month before.

Further, management should be very strict about timely preparation of the hours record. Late reports, or ones completely forgotten, will disrupt orderly enforcement of the project control system.

Exhibit 24: Individual Hours Recap*

Individual Hours Recap

Name		unit		Unit No.
		Employee No.		Month/Year

Cost Control No.	Project Job or Budget No.	Phase	Job Name	Act-ivity Code	Week of			
				Total Hours				

_____
Supervising Officer

*Courtesy First National City Bank of New York.

The Progress Report

The Progress Report, Exhibit 25, is the primary document for evaluation of project progress and for developing new estimates. A Progress Report should be prepared whenever a project checkpoint is reached. It contains information on man-hours budgeted and spent, dollars budgeted and spent, and estimates of percent completion. The figures for budgeted time and cost can be obtained from the Estimate Summary. The figures for cumulative time and cost can be found in the previous Progress Report. Information on the current month's time expenditures comes from the Individual Hours Recap. A month's computer costs are derived by multiplying the month's computer usage by the standard rates.

The Progress Report also requires an estimate of the percent complete to date of each of the phases or tasks of the project. This is an important estimate, for upon it will rest the new estimates and schedules. The best way to estimate a percent complete is to obtain an estimate of the time remaining on a task from the person working on it. Then compute the estimated percent complete by the following formula:

$$\text{Estimated percent complete} = \frac{\text{Time to date}}{\text{Time to date} + \text{estimated time to complete}}$$

While it has been found that programmers and analysis are poor estimators of percent complete (especially when percent complete is higher than 85%), the results obtained by having them estimate time remaining have been good. After the Progress Report has been reviewed against the Project Task Plan and Schedule (Exhibit 23), new time and cost estimates can be developed, using only the new estimates of percent complete and the actual time and cost to date, by the method of Chapter 13, "Review and Progress Analysis." They are now used on the development of a new schedule.

If PERT or another automatic scheduling technique is used, the system should allow for the entry of partial-completion information. The system will re-evaluate the earliest and latest times for activities, recompute slack, and produce a new schedule.

The Individual Hours Recap, after the Progress Report has been prepared from it, should be filed in the staff member's personnel file. Progress Reports become part of the permanent project file.

Exhibit 25: Progress Report

Project No. _____ Project Name _____ Supervisor _____ Date _____

Phase or Unit of Project	RESOURCE	ORIGINAL ESTIMATE		THIS PERIOD		CUMULATIVE			TO COMPLETION	
		Days	Dollars	Days	Dollars	Est. of % Compl.	Days	Dollars	Days	Dollars

17/ CONTROL SYSTEM OPERATING DOCUMENTATION

In addition to the control documents for project initiation and progress reporting, there are several more which will be of particular use in project control during various phases of the system development process. They are

— Project Review Form,
— Checkpoint Report,
— Monthly Operator Report,
— Monthly Equipment Usage Report, and
— Completed Project Report.

Project Review Form

The Project Review Form, Exhibit 26, is a summary document for recording the results of the analysis of the Progress Report. It is also useful as a summary for management. The form provides for an analysis of differences between the due date of tasks in progress and the slippage anticipated. A collection of these Review Forms over a period of time gives a valuable record of the causes of failure to meet schedule, the corrective action taken (or corrective action that was not taken), and the results.

It should be prepared by the project manager and filed with the corresponding Progress Report in the permanent project file.

Checkpoint Report

The Checkpoint Report, Exhibit 27, is a summary analysis of the project checkpoints. The two documents used in preparing it are the checkpoint list, drawn up during the project planning phases (see

Exhibit 26: Project Review Form

Part I

Project Name	Project Number	Date Prepared
Week Ending	Priority	Prepared by

Part 2

Tasks in Progress	Man-Days Scheduled This Week	Man-Days	Plus or Minus	Due Date	Slippage Anticipated	Remarks

Part 3

Tasks to Be Started Next Week

Chapter 9), and the latest Progress Reports. It should be completed at regular intervals throughout the project.

After entering the standard identification data at the top of the form, the reviewer lists the checkpoints which were due during the period, the ones actually reached, an indication of whether a quality check was involved, the checkpoints which were *not* reached, and an estimate of the calendar days to complete those not reached.

The most important use of this report is in drawing attention to problem areas. An explanation should be attached for each checkpoint listed as due but not reached, with a plan to recover lost ground. Merely identifying problem areas, however, is not enough. Data Processing management must review these forms and take *prompt action*, first to correct the difficulty, and second to ensure that it will not recur. The value of project control is in drawing attention to problems.

The Checkpoint Report should be prepared by the project manager and reviewed by the data processing manager and the automation committee. It should be filed with the working papers for the project until all difficulties shown in it have been dealt with.

Monthly Operator Report

The Operator Report, Exhibit 28, shows the time in hours each computer operator has spent on each of the projects under development and in production. It may be prepared either by the operations manager or the systems and programming manager, working from time and equipment logs kept by the operations department. Total hours should be summarized by project as well as by operator.

The Operator Report has several uses. First, it will enable management to calculate the cost of the man-time in the operations department devoted to each system, which when added to the machine operation cost (the next report to be discussed), will give the total cost of compiling and testing for the reporting period. Obvious variances from plan should be investigated. It is used in preparing the Resource Requirements Forecast, and will also serve as reference during systems testing and post-implementation evaluation of the system, at the checkpoints for operating efficiency.

Monthly Equipment Usage Report

Like the previous document, the Equipment Usage Report, Ex-

Exhibit 27: Checkpoint Report

Estimated Review Date _____

Actual Review Date _____

Project Number _____   Project Name _____

Date _____

Reviewed by _____

Checkpoints Due This Period	Checkpoints Reached This Period	Quality Check Completed	*Checkpoints Due But Not Reached	Estimated Calendar Days To Complete

*Must be supported by plan to recover.

Attendees:

Next review date _____

Exhibit 28: Monthly Operator Report

Date _____

Name	Project No.	Project Name	Hours This Month	Total

Exhibit 29: Monthly Equipment Usage Report

Date _____

Resource	Project No.	Project Name	Hours of Use This Month	Total

Exhibit 30: Completed Project Report

Project Name _____ Project Number _____

Date _____ Prepared by _____

Project Phase	Original Estimate	Actual	Loss (Gain)	Remarks
1. Systems Analysis and Design				
a. Analyst Man-Hours				
b. Programmer Man-Hours				
c. Other Man-Hours				
d. Contractor Dollars				
2. Programming & Conversion				
a. Analyst Man-Hours				
b. Programmer Man-Hours				
c. Other Man-Hours				
d. Contractor Dollars				
e. Employment Hours				
3. Installation				
a. Total Man-Hours				
b. Contractor Dollars				
c. Investment Dollars				
4. Project Due Date				

Exhibit 31: Project Control Document Checklist

Document	Exhibit	Prepared by	Assisted by	Reviewed by
User Request	18	proponent	systems analyst	data processing manager, automation committee
Resource Requirements Forecast	19	data processing manager		automation committee
System Development Estimate Guide	20	data processing manager, project manager	systems analyst	data processing manager, automation committee
Program Development Estimate Completion Form	21	project manager	systems analyst	data processing manager
Estimate Summary	22	project manager		data processing manager
Project Task Plan and Schedule	23	project manager		data processing manager, automation committee
Individual Hours Recap	24	project team members		project manager
Progress Report	25	project manager	team members	data processing manager, automation committee

Project Review Form	26	project manager		data processing manager, automation committee
Checkpoint Report	27	project manager	team members	data processing manager
Monthly Operator Report	28	operations department		project manager
Monthly Equipment Usage Report	29	operations department		project manager
Completed Project Report	30	project manager	data processing manager	data processing manager, automation committee

hibit 29, is prepared from logs kept by the operations department. It gives a summary by project of the time used on the various work stations in the computer operations department. It should be used to make sure machine cost for the development project is reasonably in line with that originally estimated (Chapter 9.) As with all other estimates, figures for continuing phases of the project should be re-examined and adjusted as necessary at each checkpoint.

This document is also used when preparing the Resource Requirements Forecase.

Completed Project Report

The Completed Project Report, Exhibit 30, provides an important historical summary of the project. It contains a listing of the phases of the project; original estimates for each phase, in dollars or man-hours, as appropriate; the actual cost in dollars or man-hours; and remarks relating to differences between estimated and actual costs. The figures and remarks should be filled in on the form as the project progresses, to create a reliable historical record with remarks written while they are current.

The Completed Project Report provides a reliable guide to what can be learned that will be useful in later projects. Examples include whether estimating techniques are producing reasonable results, and the corrective actions taken and their effects.

Project Control Document Checklist

Exhibit 31 is a checklist of the documents illustrated in this section.

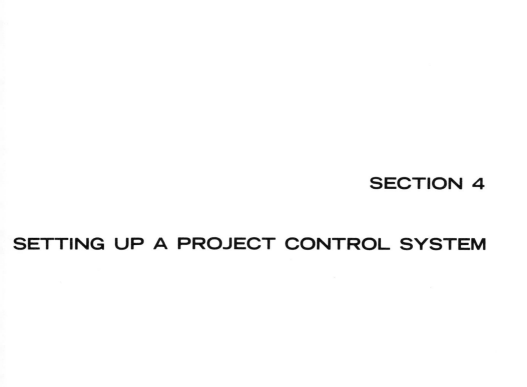

SECTION 4

SETTING UP A PROJECT CONTROL SYSTEM

18/ PREPARATORY TASKS

Establishing a project control system is a project in itself, requ‚
ing planning by management and adequate follow-up. Installation has
three stages: preparation, development and post-implementation. The
preparatory stage consists of planning for the establishment of the
system and of assessing objectives. The second stage is development
of the project control manual and the installation of the project control
system. The final stage consists of review of the effectiveness of the
system and system maintenance.

As with any other project, the automation committee should assess
the implications of establishing the project control system, considering
cost justification, anticipated benefits, and the availability of resources.
A priority should also be assigned to the project, so that it competes
fairly with all others under development and planned.

When authorization for the project has been received, the planning
stage begins. Preparatory tasks discussed in this chapter fall into three
categories,

— preparation of the development plan,
— establishment of a review committee and the project team, and
— study by the project team of the installation's project control
   needs and definition of specific objectives.

The technique of developing a project plan and schedule was discussed in Section 2 .

A working committee should be organized to prepare the development plan. It will be necessary to

— define the charter of the committee,
— assign committee members and their responsibilities, and establish working methods.

This committee may, in fact, be the automation committee itself, or it
may be a group established for the specific purpose of review of de-

velopment of the project control system. It should include representatives from operations management, system and programming management, and operations research management. A top corporate official might also be included.

Then the personnel who will develop the manual and install the system are assigned. The coordination procedures between the committee, its members, and working personnel are also defined.

One recurring problem of implementing project control systems is that of securing cooperation and acceptance from data processing personnel. A control system usually requires tighter discipline, more formal reporting steps, and more thorough documentation requirements. One approach to securing such support is to provide an opportunity for analysts and programmers to contribute to the development of the control system, by including leading members of the staff in the study group soliciting suggestions from other employees. The project team should comprise specialists in each function to ensure that all special interests and problems are considered.

The study of the installation's environment and requirements is one of the most important tasks in the entire project. It should be neither hurried nor superficial, for the ultimate success of the project control system will depend on it.

The past and present project mix should be reviewed by the study group to determine what the points of emphasis in the project control system should be. Systems documentation and project plans, budgets, and documents showing estimated versus actual man-days should be gathered. The study may go back for several years, if data is available.

All projects on which information is available should then be classified by

— purpose,
— development time, and
— use.

Projects should also be identified by type — long-term development, short-term development, modification, maintenance, and rescue maintenance. (Definitions of project types were given in Chapter 4.) The resulting statistics will provide an outline of the project environment.

To further define the working environment for the project control system, the study team should gather information about documentation and methods standards officially or unofficially in use. It is particularly important to identify standards which at present are *not* being complied with, and to attempt to determine why they are not. Knowing the reasons for their failure, whether or not they have anything to do with project control, will be a decided advantage in devising a project control system that *does* work.

The project team should then study the installation's project fulfillment performance, based on the documents gathered, for a representative period, selecting typical projects, to identify strengths and weaknesses in present controls and focus project effort on critical deficiencies. The analysis should include

- an examination of the amount and type of program maintenance being performed.
- comparison of budget to actual resource expenditures,
- comparison of time estimates to actual elapsed time, and
- review of operations and user problems.

Analysis of these factors will provide a picture of the problems and the areas most in need of control.

The study group should also review and define external policies which may affect the project control system. To do this, they will require time and cooperation from data processing management and top corporate management. The effort should be coordinated through the automation committee. Similarly, they should identify current policies and procedures internal to the data processing department, as outlined previously.

The results of the study should then be documented, with particular emphasis on the needs of the installation in light of the data processing and corporate environment within which it operates. The report should highlight conflicts which were found. These conflicts might exist between current procedures and the installation's needs; between corporate policy and present procedures; or between informal and formal practices. These conflicts should be resolved before further work is done on the project control system.

The study group might also make specific recommendations about the scope and nature of the project control system; for example, they might determine whether any individual projects or types of projects should be exempt from project control procedures.

To summarize, preparatory tasks include setting up the project team, study of the environment and needs of the installation, and documentation of the study results in a report for review by the project control review committee and/or the automation committee.

When conflicts have been resolved and authorization received for the next phase of the project, the project manager should then develop a detailed schedule, review the work to be performed, and determine the resources required for the remaining portions of the project, just as these tasks would be performed for any other project in the data processing department.

The next phase will result in the development of a project control manual, discussed in Chapter 19.

19/ THE PROJECT CONTROL MANUAL

The project control manual will be the heart of the project control system. It is for the use of all personnel in the data processing department, and contains descriptions of the procedures to be used and sample copies of the forms to be used for scheduling and reporting. Every person in the data processing department should be issued a copy of the manual.

Writing a Project Control Manual and establishing a Project Control System may be part of a larger standards effort, which solves several problems. Standards provide the much-needed yardstick for making estimates and for evaluating performance of personnel and machines, and the installation period for the standards provides a desirable environment for implementation of project control procedures. (The necessity of data processing standards to the success of a project control system was discussed in Chapter 3.) Whether or not the development of a project control system is to be part of a total standards effort, the project control manual may be a separate document, or it may be a section of the installation's data processing standards handbook.

Steps in developing the manual are:
— define the table of contents,
— assign priorities to chapter development,
— prepare content outline,
— write the chapters in the sequence previously determined,
— install system on a test basis, and
— review and modify manual.

The Table of Contents

The first step in writing the manual is to develop a table of contents. The manual may be divided into sections which correspond

Exhibit 32: Project Control Manual: Suggested Table of Contents

Introduction
1.0 Environment and Organization
    1.1 Automation Committee Functions
    1.2 Definitions of Project Phases
    1.3 Definitions of Project Types
    1.4 Designation of Managerial Responsibilities
    1.5 Standards for Specifying Project Type
    1.6 Standard Control Checkpoints by Project Type
2.0 Project Initiation
    2.1 Initiating Requests
    2.2 Authorization Procedure
    2.3 The Priority System
    2.4 Planning Procedures
    2.5 Standard Estimating and Scheduling Procedures
    2.6 Guidelines for Establishing Checkpoints
3.0 Project Monitoring
    3.1 Responsibilities
    3.2 Conducting Reviews at Checkpoints
    3.3 Conducting Reviews at Periodic Reporting Points
    3.4 Guidelines for Corrective Action
4.0 Project Control Documentation
5.0 Post-Implementation Evaluation Procedures

with the phases of system development as outlined in Chapter 4. Such an organization permits users of the system to refer quickly to the section of the manual relating to the step in development on which they are then working. In one place will be found all the standard procedures, checklists, and responsibilities for that section of the project control system.

A slightly different approach is the one suggested in Exhibit 32. In this, the sections of the manual are divided into environment and organization, project initiation, project monitoring, documentation, and post-implementation evaluation procedures. While this organization corresponds more or less to the phases of the system development process, the notable exception is that all project control documentation is grouped together in one section. The user of the manual may thus find the *procedures* he is interested in one place, which will then refer him to the associated *documentation* if he wishes to see the samples. A reference chart relating the steps of the system development process to relevant sections of the manual should be included at the beginning of the first section.

Whatever organization is chosen, care should be taken that all relevant aspects are covered, and that liberal use is made of references. Each section should begin with a list of other portions of the the manual which the user may wish to consult for related material.

Priorities for Chapter Development

After the table of contents has been prepared, reviewed, and approved, priorities should be assigned for the sequence of development. It is usually neither practical nor possible to begin at the beginning and write until the end is reached: careful consideration should be given to the sequence for writing.

Two types of priorities are recommended,

— functional sequence, and
— development sequence.

The functional sequence refers to the order of development as needed by the installation. For example, it might be decided that the chapter on "Responsibilities" should be developed first; it would include the staff reporting procedures (Individual Hours Recap) which staff members could begin preparing before other portions of the project control system are installed. Or, the needs of the installation might require that project initiation procedures (the User Request and so on,) be improved as soon as possible. In that case, those portions of the manual would be assigned the highest functional priority.

The development sequence refers to the easiest and most convenient order in which the chapters might be written from the point of view of the team doing the writing. In this case, the definition of project phases and types would come first, as almost everything else is related to that; next would come the sections having to do with the automation committee, including the priority system. Availability of various staff members to do the writing might also influence development priority. The section on documentation, if it is done as suggested in Exhibit 32, would be developed gradually, each document being defined and a sample drafted as the corresponding procedures written.

The two types of priorities, taken together, define the actual sequence in which the chapters should be written.

Content Outline

As the work on each chapter or section is taken up, the first responsibility of the writer is to prepare an outline of what the chapter will contain. This serves two purposes: to clarify the writer's thoughts about what he is going to say and where he is going to find any information he needs, and to give the review body an opportunity to see what will actually be included in each chapter before the full-scale writing effort commences. Any changes to details of the project control system or to organization of the manual are much easier to make at this point than later on.

The writer first prepares a detailed outline of the chapter. He then writes a paragraph or two about each sub-section, specifying what it is about and what documents, check-lists, and exhibits are to be included. The content outline will then serve him as a guide when he begins the full-scale draft.

Writing

Because a number of different people will probably be doing the actual writing, it is well to define in advance the style of the manual. The use of lists, diagrams, flow-charts and the like should be encouraged. Narrative passages should be brief and to the point. Direction should be given, in most cases, through the use of an imperative rather than a descriptive mode; for example, say "Enter the project number on the first line of the form" rather than "Project number should be entered," etc. A clear distinction should be made, however, between *requirements* for project control and *suggestions* for techniques to be used.

Test Installation

When the writing is substantially complete, the document should be studied by the review comittee to

— validate the workability of each procedure,
— determine weaknesses or omissions,
— determine exceptions, and
— verify that all forms and exhibits are assembled.

When the manual draft has been approved, the project control system should be tested in two steps:

1. Apply the forms and estimating techniques to a project that has been completed and then validate estimates and control

points against actual past performance. This test should provide some insignt into the workability of the system and should show the effects that could have been expected if the proper controls had been exercised.

2. Apply the system to a new project of reasonable size and complexity, using all forms, procedures, and checkpoints. To ensure the validity of the test, project standards for documentation and other project tasks must be enforced throughout the selected project. If the project mix is highly varied, several projects may be required for an adequate sampling. The practicality and timeliness of the control procedures may thus be evaluated and refinements can be made prior to release of the system for general use.

Revise the preliminary project control system manual based on test experience. Adjustments to forms, procedures, and estimating factors may be required and must be reflected in the system manual.

The formal procedure recommended for revisions to the manual is explained in detail in Chapter 21, "Post-Implementation Tasks and Maintenance." The next chapter discusses implementation procedures for the new project control system.

20/ INSTALLATION

When the Project Control Manual is being written, a plan should be drawn up for installation of the new system. When adjustments to the system, and correspondingly to the manual, have been made as a result of the pre-installation tests which were described in the last chapter, actual installation may take place. The tasks to be accomplished by the project team are to

— prepare a schedule for implementation,
— assign responsibilities for installation tasks, and
— conduct training of data processing staff.

Staff members will, of course, have become somewhat familiar with the idea of the new project control system while the manual is being prepared. They must, however, be formally trained in the use of the manual and their responsibility for executing the control system. It is strongly advised that copies of the manual be ready for all staff members to review well before the official implementation date. All staff members must be oriented to the system through training sessions and distribution of materials. Meetings should be conducted at which questions concerning the system may be raised informally. It also may be desirable to prepare a brief orientation for major users of data processing services to inform them of their roles.

It is also desirable that an adequate supply of all new forms be obtained, and ready for use on the implementation date. Sample copies of all these should be distributed to staff members at one of the orientation meetings, even though samples are also included in the manual itself. This will ensure that proper attention is given to the new forms.

Installation of the system requires extra management attention during the installation period and immediately after. The use of proper forms must be monitored and enforced, as must the development of required documentation. Adequate project time should be allotted to allow for personnel adjustment to the new approach.

An on-going task associated with the new project control manual is maintenance of the distribution record. Specific, permanent responsibility should be assigned for this task, and documented in the introductory passages of the manual itself. Exhibit 33 gives a sample of the distribution record. It implies that all copies of the manual are numbered. This is necessary for security purposes as well as for distribution. Care should be taken that all new members of the staff are issued copies of the manual, and given time to familiarize themselves with it as soon as they join the department. The distribution record is also used in conjunction with revisions, discussed in the next chapter.

Finally, throughout the planning and actual implementation period, it must be recognized by management and by the system development team that the control system should be implemented as a piece rather than in sections, and that all on-going projects should be con-

Exhibit 33: Distribution Record for Project Control Manual

Manual number	Location of recipient	Date distributed

verted to the new system at the same time, *so that exceptions do not become habitual.* After that, continued management commitment to the new control system will contribute largely to its success.

21/ POST-IMPLEMENTATION TASKS AND MAINTENANCE

As with all new systems, after four to six months of use the new project control system should be reviewed to

- determine validity of procedures, and
- determine necessity for modifications.

Methods to be used in the review include

- interview of personnel to validate applicability,
- review of documentation, and
- review of adequacy of enforcement and control methods.

The project control system is dynamic and thus requires periodic review and validation. Environmental changes, diversified project mix, and improved professional staff skills may necessitate adjustments. Permanent monitoring and administrative responsibilities for the system should be assigned for at least the first eighteen months. By that time, responsibility for the execution of the system should become a normal data processing management function. All persons affected by the system are responsible for suggesting changes or additions in accordance with the procedure outlined here.

Revision

Suggestions for revisions or additions to the system should be clearly explained in a memorandum, including

- proposer's name and other identifying information, such as department, branch, etc.,
- date and subject,
- references to affected subjects in the manual,
- explanation of the benefits to be realized, and
- suggested wording for the revisions or changes to forms.

Exhibit 34: Revision Page for Project Control Manual

Date	Page No(s).	Description of Revision	Reviser	Approval

The suggestion should be addressed to the proposer's manager, who adds his endorsement and forwards the suggestion to the manager of the data processing function. The manager of data processing should screen all suggestions and check all possible points in the system that may be affected by the change.

If the change is a significant one, the steps described in Chapter 19 for development of the system should be followed because it may be necessary to conduct research as was done when the manual was first written, to ensure that the revisions or additions will be coordinated with all affected departments. The revised manual should be similarly reviewed.

Approved revisions or additions to the manual will be published and disseminated by the data processing department. Minor changes in wording can be made in ink according to instructions on the notice of the change, but substantial changes should be reprinted and substituted for the current pages in the manual. Revised pages should be so designated, with the revision date included on the page. Replaced pages should be removed and destroyed.

A notice of change should contain

— change notice number,
— effective date of the change,
— instructions for insertion in the manual and replacement of current pages, and
— instructions on methods for instructing personnel in the new procedures or forms, if necessary.

Distribution lists should be maintained by the manager of data processing.

Revision Record Page   A revision record page should be included at the beginning of the project control system manual. Personnel designated as responsible for the manual should enter the date and change notice number and initial the entry to certify that the change has been made. A sample of such a form is given in Exhibit 34.

APPENDIX

APPENDIX

SOFTWARE PACKAGES FOR
PROJECT CONTROL

Several computer manufacturers provide program packages which purport to perform some of the functions of project control. Most, if not all, such systems apply concepts which are quite similar to those of PERT. In addition, some systems provide a mechanism for resource allocation, a vital feature of scheduling. Several manufacturer systems are described below. Information on the systems given here is as advertised by the manufacturers. Omission from this discussion of other manufacturer packages means only that relevant literature was not available for review at the time of writing.

MANAGE

Honeywell, according to its manual AN8763, "Series 200/Application Systems, *Manage* Reference Manual,"

"has developed *Manage,* a PERT-like computer software package, as a tool to be used for . . . scheduling new applications.

Pertinent implementation factors which serve as input to *Manage* include: application program identification; the number of instructions, or orders, within each program; the experience level of programmers; start and/or finish dates; complexity of the program; and the percentage of time spent on designing, programming, and testing each program. *Manage* allows the user to alter these factors as the individual situation dictates. An application status report is produced which compares actual performance to the estimated schedule at various intervals and indicates how far ahead or behind schedule the program is at the time. Based upon the information given in this report, management decisions can direct the action to be taken for optimum progress toward installation."

As in any PERT-like system, it is necessary to develop a network of events and activities in order to use *Manage*. The Manage Reference Manual contains a sample network showing the steps of systems development, and the additional activities and events that would be needed if the system were the initial application developed. These additional steps relate mainly to the requirements of ordering equipment, designing the physical layout of the installation, installing the equipment, and hiring operational personnel.

There is no resource allocation function in the *Manage* system, nor is there automatic preparation of a schedule of resource requirements. Remembering that in a PERT network logic, not resources, determines whether any two activities may proceed in parallel or must proceed sequentially, a PERT schedule can be produced which cannot be performed. Systems which have a built-in resource allocation function will usually try to reschedule each activity within its own slack (i.e., between its earliest start date and its latest start date) so as to level resources without delaying the completion date of the project. Systems not having a resource allocation capability will usually produce a report showing the resource requirements for each period so that any necessary rescheduling can be done manually. *Manage* does neither.

ASTRA

An excellent description of the problem of allocating resources to a PERT-like schedule, and adjusting the schedule as a result, is given in the General Electric manual, CPB-1041, *Automatic Scheduling With Time-Integrated Resource Allocation* (ASTRA). The System

"1. Schedules tasks to be performed, and
2. Allocates available resources to each task at the appropriately scheduled time.

"Expressed differently, ASTRA is a general purpose computer program that will assist the user in achieving maximum resource utilization with minimum project duration times and costs. Use of the ASTRA program facilitates better business decisions, improved planning and more efficient work scheduling.

"Two fundamental types of information must be provided in the ASTRA program, namely:

Activity Information — The activities denote action, and are specified in terms of a task description, precedence constraints, duration time, and resource requirements.

Resource Information — The types, quantities, and costs of available resources (both normal and overtime). Resources may consist of personnel, materials, machines, money, and space."

The activity information must be provided either in the usual PERT-like network form, or in a form called a "precedence list." The network form is the more meaningful portrayal of the project. ASTRA schedules activities and resources based upon the input information, and computes performance indicators. These are:

— "DEMAND, the total amount of each resource required by the project.
— % UTILIZATION, the efficiency of resource usage.
— MEAN UTILIZATION, the average resource usage over the duration of the project or projects.
— VARIANCE FROM MEAN, the smoothness of the resource usage over the project duration.
— COST OF DEMAND, the total cost of each resource required and used over the life of the project or projects."

The ASTRA outputs which show schedules computed by the system are available in several ways that are typical of PERT-like systems, i.e., sorted on earliest start time, latest start time, slack, float, and the like.

No provision is made in either the Honeywell or General Electric systems for optimistic, most likely, and pessimistic activity time estimates. Both systems allow for only one time estimate for each activity.

PCS/360 AND PMS/360

IBM offers at least two systems, one suitable for a very much smaller computer than the other. The former is described in Form H20-0222, *Project Control System 360 (360A-CP-06X), Application Description,* and the latter in Form H20-0210, *IBM System/360, Project Management System (360A-CP-04X), Application Description.* Despite their titles, the two systems perform only the PERT-like functions of scheduling, leaving all the other functions of project control to be performed by management.

PCS/360

The smaller system, *Project Control System/360,* offers the following major features:

- "5000 . . . activities . . . can be handled . . . The number of days in the workweek can be specified for each work item.
- For in-process work items, progress can be reported as a percent completion, or as a number of workdays remaining.
- Scheduled and actual dates can be assigned to both the beginning and end of each work item.
- Arbitrary non-workdays can be incorporated into the calendar.
- Basic resource and cost summarization capability is provided.
- Tabular and graphic reports are available."

This system accepts input either as a network or a precedence list. The cited manual contains a good description of a precedence list, and includes an example. In the usual PERT-like network, the nodes of the diagram are events, which are connected by activities; in the precedence list the nodes are activities. The IBM description of precedence lists bears out the General Electric suggestion that a PERT-like network is the more meaningful portrayal of the project.

The outputs available from PCS/360 include lists of activities sorted either by date or by float. The outputs relating to resource use can be sorted in various ways and can be produced either for one resource or for all. Other reports are available as well. The manual contains a short bibliography on PERT, CPM, and scheduling.

PMS/360

The *Project Management System/360* is described by IBM as "a highly modular set of computer program routines, each performing some function common to many management applications. It is open-ended—that is, the number of functions under PMS/360 can be expanded and added to. It is versatile—that is, the user can control program logic without resorting to reprogramming. Output reports can be defined with a simple set of procedural statements, and can be revised with every computer run if required. The computer code itself is written in a way that simplifies modification if this ever becomes necessary. At present, PMS/360 contains the following three modules: a Network Processor, a Cost Processor, and a versatile Report Processor."

The exact capabilities of this system are somewhat vague, but the manual contains an extensive bibliography of references to PERT and other project control literature.

RMS

Brandon Applied Systems has available a fully automated system for scheduling, planning, and controlling personnel and production in a data processing installation. The system is called RMS (Resource Management System), and is divided into two subsystems, only one of which is of interest here. That is the Project Control Subsystem (PCS), which is discussed extensively in Chapter 6.

RMS is designed to suit the needs of the smaller user, who may not have the computer capacity nor the management need to use one of the larger systems provided by manufacturers. Among the benefits of RMS are:

— simplicity of use,
— reduction of paperwork through automatic recordkeeping and calculation for estimating and scheduling,
— reporting of meaningful statistics for data processing management,
— regular reporting, for day-to-day control,
— on-request reporting, to provide up to the minute information for immediate decision-making,
— immediate economies resulting from more efficient allocation of machine time and personnel,
— better service to user departments,
— smoother operations by prevention of bottlenecks and anticipation of delays, and
— better planning for future needs, through trend analysis highlighted in the RMS reports.

BIBLIOGRAPHY

Recommended References

Burroughs Corporation, *PERT & CPM: Proven Tools for Management Planning & Control.* An excellent short description of PERT and PERT-COST, and cost-time balancing. Explains problem of resource allocation as related to PERT schedules, and contains a bibliography of PERT applications in such diverse fields as oil and space aeronautics.

National Cash Register Company, *Project Administration Techniques.* Very thorough discussion of ways PERT output can be helpful to management. Discusses management analysis of critical path, methods of reassigning resources to reduce length of critical path, and cost-time analyses. Bibliography.

C. W. Lowe, *Critical Path Analysis by Bar Chart,* New York: Brandon/Systems Press, 1968. Based on Critical Path Method (CPM). Deals with practical application of network methods in project control. Special merit of CPM is comparative simplicity, in that its techniques are the easier to apply the more the user insists on avoiding complications. Book shows how a simple chart technique can be applied to the planning, scheduling, and continuous control of all work involved in a project, however large it may be and however complex its character. Correctly applied, this chart technique is shown to eliminate confusion and reduce unforeseen contingencies to a minimum.

H. S. Woodgate, *Planning by Network,* New York: Brandon/Systems Press, 1968. Describes fundamental principles involved in the various systems of network planning—including PERT, CPM, and many others—and examines in detail the managerial implication of network-planning methods. Shows how networks are constructed, explains the mathematical logic of the calculations involved, and describes how the basic calculations can be performed manually or by computer. Because the book has been specifically written for those who wish to know and understand what network planning is and how to make use of this powerful management tool, the langauge used throughout is that of management and not that of the theoretician.

PERT and CPM Bibliography

Air Force Systems Command, *Concepts of PERT Cost Management,* Aeronautical Systems Division, 1962.

Ashley, William F., and Austin, Milton T., *Case Studies in Network Planning, Scheduling and Project Control for Research and Development,* Mauchly Associates, 1962.

Baker, Bruce N., "Making PERT Work," *Space Aeronautics,* March, 1962.

Barmby, John G., "The Applicability of PERT as a Management Tool," *IRE Transactions on Engineering Management,* September, 1962.

Beckwith, R. E., "A Cost Control Extension of the PERT System," *IRE Transactions on Engineering Management,* EM-9, 4, December, 1962.

Bennett, Lt.Col. John J., *Introduction to PERT/Cost,* American Management Association, June, 1962.

Berman, Herbert, "The Critical-Path Method for Project Planning and Control," *The Constructor,* September, 1961.

Bobak, E. T., "The Design, Implementation and Operation of a PERT System on a Space Program," *Aerospace Management,* March, 1963.

Booz, Allen & Hamilton, *The Management Implications of PERT,* Booz, Allen & Hamilton, 1962.

Borklund, C. W., "Is PERT All That Good?", *Armed Forces Management,* January, 1963.

Boulanger, D. G., "Program Evaluation Review Technique: Case Study Application with Analysis," *Advanced Management,* July-August, 1961.

Burgess, A. R., and Killebrew, James B., "Variation in Activity Level On a Cyclical Arrow Diagram," *Journal of Industrial Engineering,* 13, 2, March-April, 1962, 76-83.

Christensen, Borge, M., "Network Models for Project Scheduling, Part 2 – Preliminary Scheduling Phase," *Machine Design,* May 24, 1962.

Clark, Charles E., "The PERT Model for the Distribution of an Activity Time," *Operations Research,* 10, 3, May-June, 1962, 405-406.

Clark, Wallace, *The Gantt Chart,* Pitman & Sons, Ltd., 1952.

Clark, Mrs. Wallace, "The Gantt Chart," in *Industrial Engineering Handbook,* H. B. Maynard, ed., McGraw-Hill, 1956.

Collins, Thomas E., *Problems Inherent in the Design of a PERT Information and Control System,* Operations Research Inc., 1962.

Consinuke, Walter, "The Critical-Path Technique for Planning and Scheduling," *Chemical Engineering,* 69, 13, June 25, 1962, 113-118.

Department of Defense, *DOD/NASA PERT Cost Output Reports,* Supplement No.1, U.S. Government Printing Office, 1963.

———, *DOD/NASA PERT Cost Systems Design,* U.S. Government Printing Office, 1962.

Department of the Navy, *An Introduction to PERT,* Special Projects Office, 1960.

———, *Introduction to the PERT/COST System,* Special Projects Office, 1961.

———, *SP PERT Handbook,* Special Projects Office, 1965.

Federal Electric Corporation, *A Programmed Introduction to PERT,* Wiley & Sons, 1963.

Free, Raoul J., "A Generalized PERT," *Journal of the Operations Research Society of America,* March-April, 1960.

Fulkerson, D. R., and Ford, L. R., Jr., *Flows In Networks,* The RAND Corporation, 1961.

———, "A Network Flow Computation for Project Cost Curves," *Management Science,* 7, January, 1961, 167-178.

Geddes, Philip, "How Good is PERT?", *Aerospace Management,* 4, September, 1961, 41-43.

Glaser, L., and Young, R., "Critical Path Planning and Scheduling: Application to Engineering and Construction," *Chemical Engineering Progress,* 57, November, 1961, 60-65.

Glassford, W., "Critical Path Scheduling," *Plant Administration and Engineering,* 21, October, 1961, 59-62.

Gorham, William, *An Application of a Network Flow Model to Personnel Planning,* The RAND Corporation, 1960.

Healy, T. L., "Activity Subdivision and PERT Probability Statements," *Operations Research,* 9, 1961, 341-348.

Jansen, Bob, "The Use of PERT in Construction Management," *The Constructor,* January, 1962.

Jodka, John, "PERT — A Control Concept Using Computers," *Computers and Automation,* March, 1962.

Kast, W. R., "Critical Path Method Ideal Tool for Plant Construction," *Hydrocarbon Processing and Petroleum Refiner,* 41, February, 1962, 123-130.

Kelly, James E., Jr., and Walker, Morgan R., "Critical-Path Planning and Scheduling," *1959 Proceedings of the Eastern Joint Computer Conference.*

———, "Critical Path Planning and Scheduling: Mathematical Basis," *Operations Research,* 9, May, 1961, 206-210.

Kelly, James E., Jr., et al., "Using Critical Path Programming," *Automation,* 9, November, 1962.

Kester, Waldo C., "PERT vs. Management," *Armed Forces Management,* January, 1963.

Klass, Philip J., "PERT Plan Eases Management Problems," *Aviation Week,* April 10, 1961.

Levy, Ferdinand K., et al., "The ABC's of the Critical Path Method," *Harvard Business Review,* September-October, 1963.

Lewis, James, "Where PERT is Headed," *Armed Forces Management,* July, 1961.

Lowe, C. W., *Critical Path Analysis by Bar Chart,* Brandon/Systems Press, 1968.

Lunkenheimer, E. L., "Use of Critical Path Method to Plan Complex Projects," *Power Engineering,* 66, September, 1962.

Lynch, C. J., "Plan Projects Scientifically with Critical Path Scheduling," *Project Engineering,* 32, September 18, 1961.

MacCrimmon, K. R., and Ryavec, C. A., *An Analytical Study of the PERT Assumptions,* The RAND Corporation, 1962.

Mark, E. J., "How Critical Path Method Controls Piping Installation Progress," *Heating, Piping and Air Conditioning,* September, 1963.

Maynes, Walter, "What's Wrong with PERT," *Aerospace Management,* April, 1962.

McGee, Arthur A., and Markarian, Murad D., "Optimum Allocation of Research/Engineering Manpower within a Multi-Project Organizational Structure," *IRE Transactions on Engineering Man-*

agement, September, 1962.

Meder, J. J., and Phillips, C. R., *Project Management with CPM and PERT,* Reinhold, 1964.

Miller, Robert W., "How to Plan and Control with PERT," *Harvard Business Review,* March-April, 1962.

———, *Schedule Cost and Profit Control with PERT,* McGraw-Hill, 1963.

Moshman, J., et al., "RAMPS, A Technique for Resource Allocation and Multiproject Scheduling," *Proceedings of the AFIPS 1963 Spring Joint Computer Conference.*

National Aeronautics and Space Administration, *NASA PERT and Companion Cost System—Handbook,* Office of Programs.

O'Brien, J. J., *CPM in Construction Management,* McGraw-Hill, 1965.

Paige, Hilliard W., "How PERT-Cost Helps the General Manager," *Harvard Business Review,* November-December, 1963.

Paskman, Martin, and Livingston, J. Sterling, "Is PERT What Management Needs?—No—Yes—," *Aerospace Management,* October, 1962.

PERT Coordinating Group, *PERT Guide for Management Use,* U.S. Government Printing Office, 1963.

Peterson, R. J., "Critical Path Scheduling for Construction Jobs," *Civil Engineering,* 32, August, 1962, 44-47.

Phelps, H. Sheldon, "What Your Key People Should Know About PERT," *Management Review,* October, 1962.

Pocock, J. W. "PERT As An Analytical Aid for Program Planning— Its Payoff and Problems," *Operations Research,* 10, 6, November-December, 1962, 893-903.

Roseboom, J., et al., "Application of a Technique for Research and Development Program Evaluation," *Operations Research,* September-October 1959.

Shaffer, L. R., et al., *The Critical Path Method,* McGraw-Hill, 1965.

Simms, T.J.G., "Critical Path Method—An Appraisal of the Construction Scheduling Technique," *Engineering and Contract Record,* June, 1961.

Simon, C., "Standardization: The Key to Making PERT Work," *Operations Research,* 9, 1961.

Sobszak, Thomas, "A Look at Network Planning," *IRE Transactions Engineering Management,* EM-9, 3, September, 1962.

Steinfeld, R. C., "Critical Path Saves Time and Money," *Chemical*

Engineering, 67, November 28, 1960, 148-152.

Stenger, C. B., "Scheduling Projects by Critical Path," *Electronics,* March 2, 1962.

Stires, David M., and Wenig, Raymond, *Concept — Principles — Applications PERT/Cost,* Industrial Education Institute.

Thompson, Robert E., "PERT — Tool for R and D Project Decision Making," *IRE Transactions on Engineering Management,* September, 1962.

Thompson, V., "PERT: Pro and Con About This Technique," *Data Processing,* October, 1961.

U.S. Air Force, *USAF-PERT, Volumes I-V,* ASFC PERT Control Board Headquarters (SCCS).

Woodgate, H. S., *Planning By Network,* Brandon/Systems Press, 1968.

Wynne, B. E., Jr., "Critical Path Method: An Effective Management Tool," *Controller,* 30, June, 1962, 258-264.

Young, Lewis H., "How Industry Schedules by Computer," *Control Engineering,* 9, 1, January, 1962, 16-18.

Application of PERT Planning to Public Works Maintenance Projects. Public Works Department, U.S. Naval Air Station, Port MUGU, California.

Automatic Data Processing Glossary, American Bankers Association.

"Communications Shorthand for Management: The Critical Path Techniques," *Steel,* 1, 51, November 9, 1962, 74-78.

Computers and Operations Research in Road Building, Case Institute of Technology, 1957.

"Critical Path Planning Means More Economical Turnarounds," *Oil and Gas Journal,* 58, 23, June 6, 1960.

"Faster Phased Plan Speeds Plant Building," *Chemical Weekly,* August 26, 1961.

"Million-Dollar Movers," *Chemical Week,* June 9, 1962.

"New Tool for Job Management," *Engineering News Record,* 166, January 26, 1961, 25.

"Optimum Allocation of Resources Among the Activities of a Network," *Journal of Industrial Engineering,* January, February, 1961.

"PERT — An Automated Research and Development Management Information System," *Proceedings of the 12th Annual National American Industrial Engineering Conference,* 1961.

"PERT (Program Evaluation and Review Technique) — A Control Concept Using Computers," *National Accountant's Association*

Bulletin, 43, 5, January, 1962.

"PERT Cost System Design Moves Toward Uniform Procedures," *Management Review,* July-August, 1962.

"PERT—A Designed Management Information System," *Industrial Management,* 3, June, 1961, 23-32.

PERT Manual, American Institute of Industrial Engineers, 1962.

PERT—A New Management Planning and Control Technique, American Management Association, 1962.

PERT Summary Report—Phase 1, PERT Summary Report—Phase 2, Special Projects Office, Bureau of Naval Weapons, 1961.

"PERT: What It Is; What It Can Do For You," *Systems Management,* July, 1962.

"Use of PERT/Cost," *Business Week,* July, 1962.

Project Control
Bibliography

Bloom, Dr. William, "Management Control Techniques Direct Decision Making," *Aerospace Management,* December, 1961.

Boehm, George A. W., "Helping the Executive Make Up His Mind," *Fortune,* April, 1962.

Booth, Andrew D., "Innovations and Applications," *Automatic Data Processing,* April, 1959.

Brandon, Dick H., *Management Standards for Data Processing,* D. Van Nostrand, 1963.

Bridgeman, P. T., "How to Make a Feasibility Study," *Automatic Data Processing,* March, 1960.

Burnham, Edward P., "Controlling the Costs of Research," *Management Review,* August, 1958.

Callahan, Joseph M., "New Planning Tool Explored," *Automotive News,* April 29, 1963.

Camp, William E., "Executive Direction of Projects," in *Handbook of Industrial Research Management.* Carl Heyel, ed., Reinhold Publishing Corporation, 1959.

Campise, J. A., "Advanced Management in Data Processing," *Journal of Data Management,* 1, June, 1963, 46-49.

Chorafas, Dimitris N., *Operations Research for Industrial Management,* Reinhold Publishing Corporation, 1958.

Cole, K. C., "Let's Put the Data Processing Manager Where He Belongs," *DPMA Quarterly,* 2, 3, April, 1966, 14-19.

Conway, B. J., et al., *Business Experience with Electronic Computers,* Controllers Institute Research Foundation, 1959.

Coughlin, William J., "Management of Mediocrity," *Missiles and Rockets,* April 15, 1963.

Cuilliton, James W., "Diagram of Management Control," *Harvard Business Review*, March-April, 1960.

Daniel, Ronald D., "EDPM — Getting Past the Barriers to Success," *The Controller*, December, 1958.

Davidson, H. O., "The Management, Engineering and Scientific Functions," *The Journal of Industrial Engineering,* 11, 2, March-April, 1960.

Denz, Ronald F., "Auditing the Data Processing Department," *DPMA Quarterly,* 3, 3, April, 1967, 24-44.

Diebold, John, "Office Automation: Is Management Getting Its Money's Worth?", *Management Review,* September, 1958.

Doyle, G. A., "Modern Management Systems — Their Impact on Construction Contractors," *The Constructor,* July, 1967.

Drucker, Peter F., "Thinking Ahead: Potential of Management Science," *Harvard Business Review,* January-February, 1959.
————, *The New Management Tools and What the Manager Can Expect of Them,* American Management Association.

Fazar, W., *New Techniques for Management Control,* Special Projects Office, U. S. Navy Department, 1961.

Fleming, Quentin W., and Ervin, Charles, W., "Management Aids for Program Control," *Aerospace Management,* July, 1962.

Forrester, Jay W., "Industrial Dynamics — A Major Breakthrough for Decision Makers," *Harvard Business Review,* July-August, 1958.

Goode, Harry H., "The Analogy Between the Problems of Systems Engineering and Management," *Chemical Engineering Progress,* January, 1959.

Grimes, A. J., and Vergin, R. C., "The Impact of the Computer," Report No. 5, School of Business Administration, University of Minnesota, April, 1963.

Harling, John, "Simulation Techniques in Operational Research," *Operational Research Quarterly,* March, 1959.

Head, R. V., "Testing Real-Time Systems — Part I, Development and Management," *Datamation,* 10, 8, August, 1964, 54-57.

Hollis, Cecil R., "Programming for Control of Contract Performance," *NAA Bulletin,* March, 1960.

Jones, J. P., "Data Processing Management, Is It Unique?", *Proceedings of the 2nd Annual Conf. Computer Personnel Research Group,* 103-116.

Kanter, J., "Compact, A New EDP Management Tool," *Journal of Data Management,* 2, 6, June 1964, 38-43.

Keller, Arnold E., "EDP — Power in Search of Management," *Business Automation,* 13, 6, June, 1966, 46-52.

Klein, Herbert E., "Psychoanalysis on the Production Line," *Dun's Review and Modern Industry Magazine*, February, 1962.

Laubach, Peter B., *Company Investigations of Automatic Data Processing,* Harvard University Graduate School of Business Administration, 1957.

Lecht, Charles Philip, *The Management of Computer Programming Projects*, American Management Association, 1967.

Livingston, J., "The New Management Elite," *Journal of Armed Forces Management Association*, 1961.

MacLean, J. D., "Caution: Crash Computer Conversion," *Systems and Procedures Journal,* 18, 1, January-February, 1967, 8-11.

Malcolm, D. G., et al., "Application of a Technique for Research and Development Program Evaluation," *Operations Research,* 7, 5, September-October, 1959, 646-669.

Malcolm, D. G., "A Designed Management Information System," *Industrial Management*, June, 1961.

————, "System Simulation: A Fundamental Tool for Industrial Engineering," *The Journal of Industrial Engineering,* 9, 3, 1958.

————, "Management Control Systems", Wiley & Sons, 1960.

McCloskey, Joseph F., and Trefethen, Florence N., eds., *Operations Research for Management,* The Johns Hopkins University Press, 1954.

Mundorff, G. T., and Bloom, William, *Managing a Development Program*, General Precision, Inc., 1960.

Muth, J. F., and Thompson, G. L., *Industrial Scheduling*, Prentice-Hall, 1963.

Nelson, E. A., *Management Handbook for the Estimating of Computer Programming Costs*, System Development Corporation, 1967.

Patrick, R. L., "A Technique for Improving the Management of a Computer Installation, *DPMA Quarterly,* 4, July, 1965, 2-31.

Postley, John A., *Computers and People*, McGraw-Hill, 1960.

Quinn, J. B., *Yardsticks for Industrial Research*, The Ronald Press, 1959.

Rafferty, James A., "Do These Management Systems Fit Together?", Aerospace Management, May, 1962.

Sasieni, Maurice, et al., *Operations Research, Methods and Problems,* Wiley & Sons, 1959.

Sisson, R. L., "Sequencing in Job Shops — A Review," *Operations Research,* January-February, 1959.

U.S. Air Force, "A Summary of Lessons Learned from Air Force Management Surveys," *AFSCP 375-2,* Air Force Systems Command, June, 1963.

U.S. Army Material Command Headquarters, "Planning and Control Techniques and Procedures (PCT)" *ARMC 11-16,* Rock Island Arsenal.

Villers, Raymond, "The Scheduling of Engineering Research," *Journal of Industrial Engineering,* 10, 6, November-December, 1959.

Wall, Eugene, "Information Systems," *Chemical Engineering Progress,* January, 1959.

Weber, C. Edward, "Change in Managerial Manpower with Mechanization of Data Processing" *Journal of Business,* April, 1959.

Weil, J. W., "The Impact of Time-Sharing on Data Processing Management," *DPMA Quarterly,* 2, 2, January, 1966, 2-16.

Wilson, Randle C., "Problems of R & D Management," *Harvard Business Review,* January-February, 1959.

Wofsey, M. M., "Managing the Computer Department," *Systems Management,* 4, 6, November-December, 1963, 13-17, 26.

"Fresh Attack on Rising Costs," *Armed Forces Management,* February, 1960.

"New Way to Analyze and Plan Operations and Projects Will Save You Time and Cash," *Oil/Gas World,* 3, September, 1959, 38-46. 38-46.

"Real-Time Management Control in a Large-Scale Man-Machine System," *The Journal of Industrial Engineering,* March-April, 1960.

"Relief for the Harried Job Estimator," *Business Automation,* 11, 5, May, 1964, 30-34.

"Shortcut for Project Planning," *Business Week,* July 7, 1962.

"Splurge of Research is Piling Up New Problems for Management," *Business Week,* January 4, 1958.